Printed in the United Kingdom

First Printing, 2017
Reprinted, 2017

ISBN: 978-0-9573199-8-1

Sea Salt Publishing
Bournemouth, Dorset
BH4 8ER

seasaltlearning.com
julianstodd.wordpress.com

TABLE OF CONTENTS

© Julian Stodd

into the Social Age

INTRODUCTION

Social Leadership is a style of leadership fit for the Social Age, the world of constant change we live in today. It's a form of authority earned within our communities, contextual, consensual and founded upon our social reputation. It can complement our formal authority, within a hierarchy, but it's also available to those with no formal power whatsoever.

Social Leaders help an organisation to thrive, by connecting the power of the community to the everyday challenges of work. For an organisation to become Socially Dynamic, it's essential: 'Socially Dynamic' is a state of embedded agility, a broad-based capacity for change.

Social Leadership is built upon humility, fairness and kindness, but it's no soft form of power: it's a power that is earned and, because of that, it carries great weight. It's built upon trust.

This book provides a practical journey to becoming a Social Leader: it's structured to ask one question, or offer one provocation, every day.

It takes us through the foundations, then on to the nine elements of the NET Model, each one lasting two weeks, that cover the specific skills of Social Leadership.

This is not the whole journey, but if you follow this pathway, in 14 weeks' time, you will have set the foundations for becoming a strong Social Leader.

Julian Stodd
2017

The
NET
Model
of
Social
Leadership

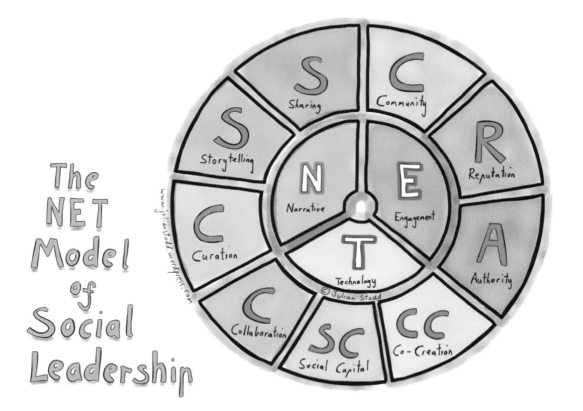

www.julianstodd.wordpress.com

S Sharing
C Community
S Storytelling
R Reputation
N Narrative
E Engagement
C Curation
T Technology
A Authority
C Collaboration
SC Social Capital
CC Co-Creation

© Julian Stodd

THE NET MODEL

The NET Model is both a description of and a developmental journey towards Social Leadership. It takes us through three core areas: 'Narrative', which is about how we find our space, and shape our story, 'Engagement', which is about our communities and the ways we find Social Authority, and 'Technology', which is about co-creation, the ways we collaborate, and the need to build Social Capital in ourselves and others.

Let's consider the nine elements in more detail, as they form the story of Social Leadership:

NARRATIVE
- » **CURATION** is about finding your space
- » **STORYTELLING** is about understanding narratives and power
- » **SHARING** is about adding to the signal, not just making more noise

ENGAGEMENT
- » **COMMUNITY** looks at our visible and hidden communities and the roles we serve within them
- » **REPUTATION** explores how our actions have impact, and how we influence this
- » **AUTHORITY** is about types of power, and those that are awarded to us, if we earn it

TECHNOLOGY
- » **CO-CREATION** explores the co-creative process that takes place in communities
- » **SOCIAL CAPITAL** is our prerequisite, to drive for equality and fairness in everything we do
- » **COLLABORATION** is both the pinnacle and the start of Social Leadership

THE SOCIAL AGE

I use the term 'Social Age' to describe the ecosystem we inhabit today. It's characterised by broad swathes of change: the new nature of work, the democratisation of creativity and technology, social collaborative technologies, the rise of communities, and the new nature of knowledge – dynamic, adaptive and mobile.

The change is both widespread and insidious, impacting every aspect of the world around us. The impacts of this are just starting to be felt: there is a faint awareness that technology is taking us into new spaces, but it's really about far more than simply technology.

Whilst we are only at the start of the impact of the Digital Age (with the widespread exploitation of immersive and augmented reality, and wearable tech still to bite), we already feel the most pervasive effect: that we are connected. To people, to knowledge, to communities.

To survive, to hope to thrive, organisations must adapt every aspect of how they operate. This is a significant challenge: the things that got us this far will not get us the rest of the way.

I have started talking over on the blog [www.julianstodd. wordpress.com] about the Socially Dynamic Organisation: one that has a diversified strength, an ability to thrive in this time of constant change without getting breathless.

Social Leadership is one of the core traits of the Socially Dynamic Organisation: it is strong in its formal aspects (hierarchy, system and process) and strong in its social ones (humility, equality and fairness).

The Social Age is fully upon us: we must adapt to survive. And if it's not you leading the change, then who?

DAYS 1 TO 10 – FOUNDATIONS

As we start on our journey towards Social Leadership, we need to set our foundations in place. Let's take our first ten days to do that: to explore how the world has changed, and our role in building a better, a more Socially Dynamic, a fairer, organisation.

We may spend a lifetime learning how to leave a light footprint upon the world. In these one hundred days, we seek simply to start. To give ourselves time to reflect. To start our journey.

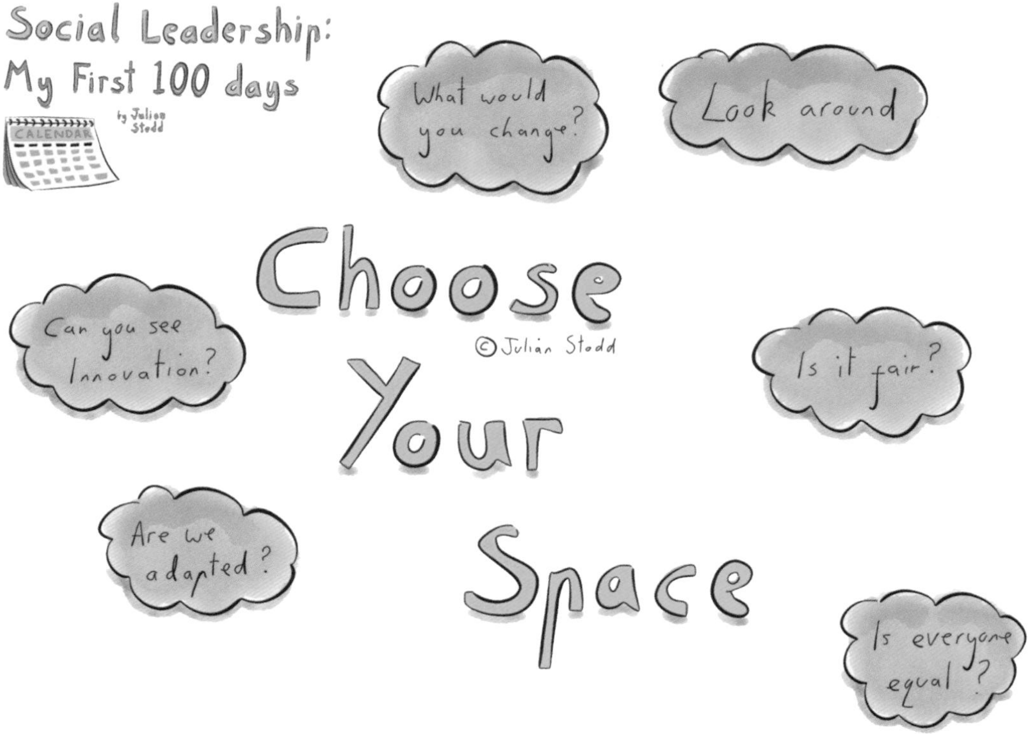
Social Leadership:
My First 100 days
by Julian Stodd
CALENDAR
What would you change?
Look around
Can you see Innovation?
Choose Your Space
© Julian Stodd
Is it fair?
Are we adapted?
Is everyone equal?

DAY 1: ARE YOU CONTENT?

Look at the organisation around you, the organisation that you work for.

» Are you content with what you see?
» Is it fair? Is it equal? Is it innovative and successful?
» Is it ready to face tomorrow?
» Is it adapted to the realities of the Social Age?
» If you could change one thing, what would it be?

I would change: _____

_____

_____

_____

Ask these questions of someone else: do you have the same answers, or different ones? Across the organisation, would your answers be the same or different? Where is the space to have these conversations? Where is your space to drive change?

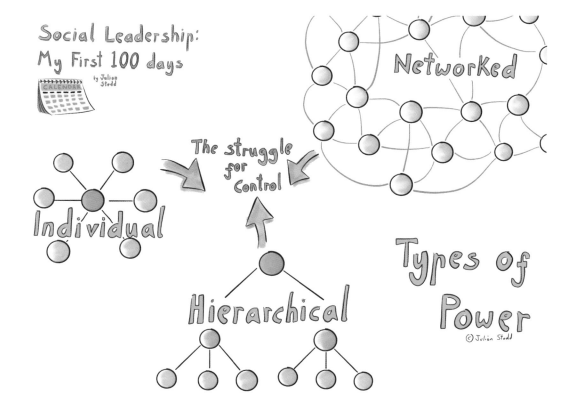

Social Leadership: My First 100 days
by Julian Stodd

Networked

The struggle for Control

Individual

Hierarchical

Types of Power
© Julian Stodd

DAY 2: POWER

Think about the thing you wanted to change: what power do you have to change that?

There are three types of power: '*Individual*' power, which we exert with people we know, '*Hierarchical*' (formal) power, which is the type of power the organisation gives us, and '*Networked*' power, which is where Social Leadership lives – power and amplification granted to us by the community.

To be the leader you need to be, which types of power do you have, and which do you need to build or earn?

My formal power lives in these places: _____

_____

_____

My networked power lives in these places: _____

_____

_____

Consider which of these you can grow. To gain more formal power, you need a promotion! To gain more Social Authority, you just need to earn it.

DAY 3: IF NOT YOU, THEN WHO?

Social Leadership is about taking action, about creating organisations and a wider society that are better: fairer, kinder, more equal, more effective, more inclusive. It's not a dream of a better world: it's the concrete steps to build it.

» Where do you see inequality?
» Where do you see unfairness?
» Where do you see a challenge, either in your organisation, or in wider society?
» Who will solve it?

Does the power to effect change lie just in formal authority, or is some of it about our ability to inspire a community to action. What is the primary type of power you wield in the world?

My formal power: _____

_____

_____

My social power: _____

_____

_____

Social Leadership:
My First 100 days
by Julian Stodd

CALENDAR

Co-Owned
© Julian Stodd

Co-Created

Adaptive

Knowledge

Evolutionary

Dynamic

DAY 4: WHERE IS THE KNOWLEDGE?

In the Social Age, knowledge itself is distributed, co-created, dynamic and adaptive. Where does knowledge live in your organisation?

> » Where do you go to find things out?

The knowledge lives in this formal place: _____

_____

_____

And in this social place: _____

_____

_____

Think about which of these spaces are formal, held in 'guides' and 'intranets', and which are social and co-created, held in people's heads or in communities.

How did you first find out where the knowledge was: through an induction programme, or through the community around you?

Social Leaders are powerful because they are connected to the tacit, tribal forms of knowledge, the lived experience, that flow through the organisation.

Social Leadership:
My First 100 days
by Julian Stodd

CALENDAR

Time

Resource

Energy

Generosity

© Julian Stodd

Spirit

Connections

DAY 5: GENEROSITY

Social Leaders help others to succeed: who can you help today, and how?

The investment we make into our community, through our generosity, is not made in expectation of immediate reciprocity, but rather to help the community grow.

I can do this: _____

_____

_____

Our Social Authority is awarded to us by the community: it's not transactional, but rather based upon the reputation that we earn.

Social Leadership:
My First 100 days
by Julian Stodd

CALENDAR

Formal
Power

Reputational
Power
© Julian Stodd

DAY 6: YOUR FORMAL POWER

List three things you are able to achieve with your formal power, the power granted to you by your position and formal role:

1. _____

2. _____

3. _____

Now list one thing you can only achieve through your reputation:

1. _____

Social Leadership is not an alternative to formal leadership: it complements it and reaches the places where formal cannot go.

Social Leadership:
My First 100 days
by Julian Stodd

What is the picture?

DAY 7: THE GIG ECONOMY

In the Social Age, we will have many different jobs in whatever passes for a '*career*'. How many jobs have you had? What about people in your team, or those around you? Ask five other people and add up their answers. What is the total number of jobs that the six of you have had?

Between us, we have had ＿＿＿＿＿＿＿＿ jobs.

This experience is part of the strength of your community. But is that picture complete? What skills is your community missing?

Social Leadership:
My First 100 days
by Julian Stodd
CALENDAR

Built

Intent

Trust
© Julian Stodd

Actions

Authenticity

Eroded

DAY 8: DO YOU TRUST ME?

In the research I have done around the Landscape of Trust, we see that 54% of people have '*low*' or '*no*' trust in the organisation that they work for. What factors build trust? And what factors erode it?

These things build trust:

1. _____

2. _____

3. _____

These things erode trust:

1. _____

2. _____

3. _____

A key role of Social Leaders is to earn the trust of those people around them, and to contribute to the overall Landscape of Trust experienced within the organisation.

To do so may require us to challenge the organisation itself, whenever we feel it lacks authenticity in its actions.

Are you ready to champion your community? Are you ready to take a stand?

Social Leadership:
My First 100 days
by Julian Stodd

CALENDAR

Is your

© Julian Stodd

Authenticity

Reflected in your Actions?

DAY 9: I DO NOT BELIEVE IT

Authenticity is an alignment of our core values to our voice and action. When communications flow through the organisation, we ask ourselves, '*do I believe this?*', '*what will be the real impact for me?*'

Those messages are sent out by people as clever and well intentioned as you and me. But sometimes we compromise our values, our integrity, because… well, because it feels like we have to. Sometimes 'we just have to do the things that we are told to do'.

It's difficult: authenticity is vital for the way our stories land, but do you always believe in the things you say and do?

Maybe you already feel you have the strength and power to be authentic. That's great: if that's how you feel, use today to ask others if they do too. Remember, Social Leaders are successful because they help others to navigate these things.

Social Leaders sometimes have to make the hard choice to do what is right, not what is easy. And that can be a harder path to follow.

Yes ☐

No ☐

Social Leadership:
My First 100 days
by Julian Stodd

Who would
you follow ?

© Julian Stodd

DAY 10: I'D FOLLOW

Who would you follow?

I would follow: _____

_____

Why would you follow them?

1. _____

2. _____

3. _____

Why would people follow you?

Social Leaders do not lead through strength, they lead through consensus, and within set contexts.

If you move beyond your formal authority, why will people follow you?

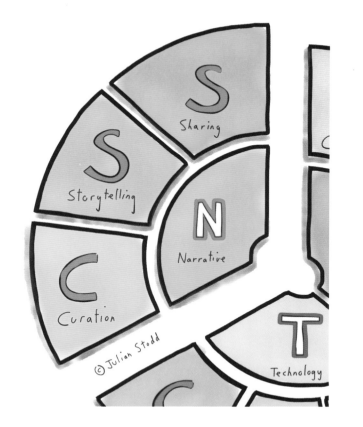

© Julian Stodd

NARRATIVE: FIND YOUR SPACE, SHAPE YOUR STORY, START THE JOURNEY

The first step to Social Leadership is to find your space: where will you earn your reputation, and what is your purpose? It's fine to evolve this over time, but you need an authentic foundation from which to act. Examples would be to be a great project manager, to be an enabler for others, to bring innovation to a stale function.

Think about how stories are used within your organisation: where are formal stories told, and where do social ones live?

Who owns the stories? Which are most valuable to you?

How can people respond to stories? How are they treated if they disagree? Does the formal try to 'own' the social?

These are all factors we need to consider when looking at Narrative in Social Leadership: where will we stand, what is our stance, how do we use stories, and how do we share them, wisely?

Social Leaders do not add to the noise: they filter to find the signal.

Social Leaders share wisely.

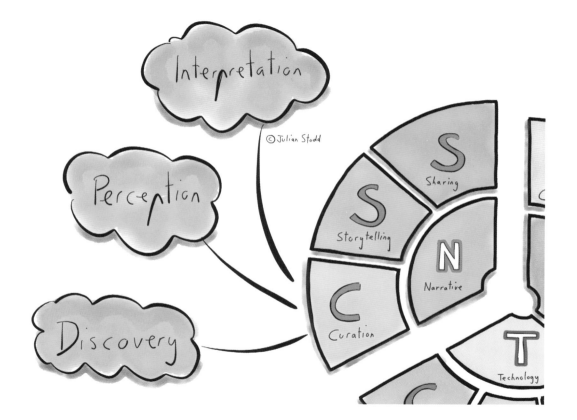

DAYS 11 TO 19: CURATION

Choose your space: what kind of Social Leader will you seek to be?

This may evolve over time, but you need to start some-where. Even the process of thinking is valuable, as it's reflective time in a busy world.

Curation lets us choose our starting line: it provides focus.

And once we have that position, we curate ideas, content, stories, around this core space. Curation is an active process: we do not simply do it once, we do it continu-ously over time.

Social Leadership:
My First 100 days
by Julian Stodd

DAY 11: WHAT WILL YOU BE KNOWN FOR?

You need to choose your space: what will you be known for? Think within your organisation:

Who is a strong leader? _____

Who is a great project manager? _____

Who do you trust most? _____

Who helps you to be successful?

_____

Who challenges you most constructively?

_____

Who is the most humble person you know?

_____

Have you thought of someone for each of these things?

Would your answers have been different if I'd said '*think outside of your organisation*'?

In the Social Age, our communities extend far and wide.

Do you think they would agree with your view? Why not ask them?

How often do we stumble into a space rather than choose to enter it?

Be proactive: be bold. Make your decision: choose your space.

Social Leadership:
My First 100 days
by Julian Stodd

The Rules
1 Positive
2 Constructive
3 Responsive

DAY 12: SETTING THE RULES

Once you have chosen your space, you need to set the rules: how will you act?

This can be very simple. I have three rules:

1. To always be positive
2. To offer constructive advice when I disagree
3. To respond to everyone who engages, whatever their energy

Those who know me will know that these are sometimes aspirational, not always my truth, but I strive for them.

When I am observing others, I try to be positive, because my energy affects others.

When I disagree, I could choose to argue, but I choose to debate, and offer support.

When people bother to engage with my thinking and actions, I try to respond, even if it's just to say 'thank you'. When I disagree with what they say or offer, I still try to say thank you, whilst being unafraid to disagree.

What would your rules be? _____

_____

_____

_____

Sometimes we break the rules, but they act as our scaffolding, our guiding principles. Reflecting upon them, questioning them, making them conscious, is a useful reflective exercise.

Social Leadership:
My First 100 days
by Julian Stodd
CALENDAR
Where Are Your Libraries?
©Julian Stodd

DAY 13: NEW LIBRARIES

Social Leaders curate great content, ideas and resources for their communities. Where are your libraries? Where do you find your new knowledge?

Think about the places you turn to for news, for learning, for knowledge.

Do you have enough spaces?

Is the content aligned to your values, the values you curated?

Is there a bias in your knowledge: do you just watch TED Talks, or read *Harvard Business Review*?

Where could you turn to to hear new views? To hear new stories?

_____

_____

_____

_____

Social Leadership:
My First 100 days
by Julian Stodd
CALENDAR
Content
© Julian Stodd
COLA
Consumption

DAY 14: GREAT LOOKING, BADLY FITTING

What content do you consume most often?

> » Podcasts
> » Videos
> » Articles
> » Images
> » Other (please specify)

Rate them in order:

1. _____

2. _____

3. _____

4. _____

5. _____

So if that's what you do, what do others do? Are you sharing great content that fits badly?

Why not ask five people, and see whether their answers match yours?

Have you taken time to think about what lands 'well', and what you get no response from?

Consider people's 'everyday reality': whilst you may be office based, are they driving (podcasts are great), working in an engineering environment (podcasts maybe not great!)?

Do you always share long articles, or short tweets?

Social Leadership:
My First 100 days
by Julian Stodd

An

Action

© Julian Stodd

Day

DAY 15: AN ACTION DAY

When we talk about '*curation*', we mean more than just '*content*': we curate ourselves as well.

We go through this active process of thinking '*what is the type of Social Leader that I want to be?*', and '*what is the journey I must make to get there?*'

Who is going to write the story of your journey?

Maybe one of the stories that you curate could be your own?

If you have ever thought about writing, blogging, getting onto Twitter, or joining a new community, today is the day to do it.

Remember: developing Social Leadership is not an academic exercise. It's about doing things differently, from day one.

What have you started to do differently since we started our voyage two weeks ago?

Curation is an active process, not a passive observation. Don't write anything in the book today: go and do something in the real world.

DAY 16: TO DISAGREE

Do you share stories that you agree with? Social Leaders have to engage in communities and spaces that they are uncomfortable with: they have to engage, with respect, to make a difference. This applies to curation too: we should share stories that we disagree with, not to ridicule them or deny them, but to learn from them and engage with them.

Find something that someone has shared with you, in your inbox, or perhaps on Facebook: find a story that you disagree with.

Can you engage with an alternative viewpoint (whilst remembering to stay true to your values, the ones we wrote earlier!)?

What story will you engage with? _____

_____

_____

How can you engage with respect? What will be your stance?

_____

_____

_____

Engaging with an alternative viewpoint, whilst offering insights and ideas, is debating. Anything else is argument or denial.

Wise leaders take pragmatic steps: they recognise that not everything will go their way, so they engage in the debate, to earn a chance for their voice to be heard.

DAY 17: AM I THE PROBLEM?

Your reputation should be something you curate, but sometimes things are imposed upon you. We are told to do things we may not agree with. Or perhaps we have simply made a mistake and are living with the consequences.

Sometimes we get swept along with the crowd.

The challenge for Social Leaders is that everything they do, whether they 'agree' with it or not, reflects on their reputation and, potentially, imposes itself on their ability to drive for fairness and equality.

Can you think of a time when you felt pushed into an uncomfortable place, when you had to do something just because you were told to? Or maybe you did it just because 'that's how it's always done'. Or perhaps you were learning, and made a mistake that you couldn't fix.

What would your example be? _____

_____

_____

_____

_____

Were you able to think of one? Or did you convince yourself that you would never do that?

How many people consciously do things that actively erode culture, are deliberately 'evil'?

Is it possible that we all do this, but just don't realise it? Make today a reflective day.

Social Leadership:
My First 100 days
by Julian Stodd

CALENDAR

Culture

Culture

Culture

Culture

Culture

Aspiration
© Julian Stodd

Culture

Culture

Culture

Culture

DAY 18: ASPIRATIONAL VALUES

There are two types of values:

1. Organisational values: these are written in the handbook and posted in the lift
2. The values we demonstrate in the grinding lived reality of our everyday

Organisations often have a slew and glut of 'official values', but are surprisingly quiet about the actual lived reality.

As Social Leaders, we need our values to be clear, not for other people, but for ourselves. Our values will give us our foundations of stone.

Nobody is perfect, but we can strive.

Do you always do the right thing?

Yes ☐

No ☐

I'm not sure I could honestly answer 'yes' to this, although I'd love to. Nobody is perfect, but we can strive to be, and the first step is to acknowledge that we can do better.

Culture is created in the grinding reality of our everyday, not the aspiration of the handbook.

As Social Leaders, we must curate our own values, and help the organisation curate its own values: lived, not aspirational.

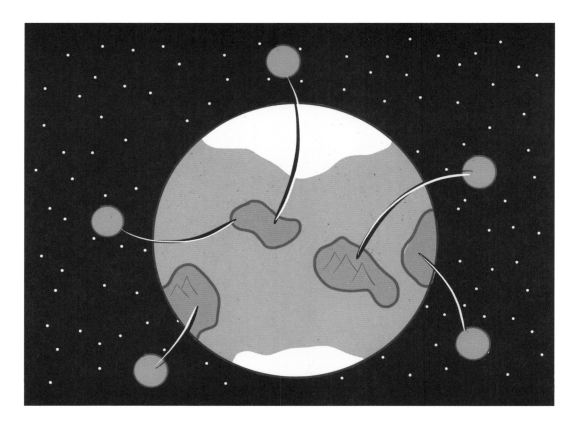

DAY 19: THE WAY YOU ARE IN THE WORLD

Curation is about choosing the space we will inhabit, the way we are in the world.

Are you clear where you want to be?

Who will your buddies be on this trip? Who do you know that you can trust, who you can be open and honest with, and who will be open and honest with you?

Perhaps they are on their own Social Leadership journey, or perhaps they are simply someone wise and kind enough to support yours.

Who will your buddy be? _____

_____

_____

My Social Leadership buddies are Valerie and Sam, both people who are striving to be better Social Leaders themselves, and who help me to be better. Not by telling me the answers, but by helping me find the ways I can be better.

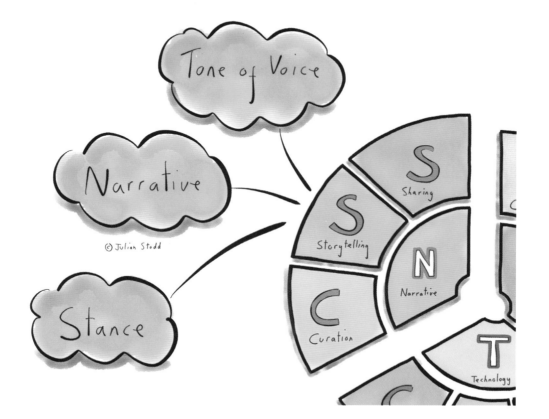

© Julian Stodd

DAYS 20 TO 29: STORYTELLING

Social Leaders are great storytellers, in formal spaces, and across social ones. They understand how stories are shaped and shared, how they are amplified, how they are magnetic, the different styles that they take, and what we can do to make our own stories spread.

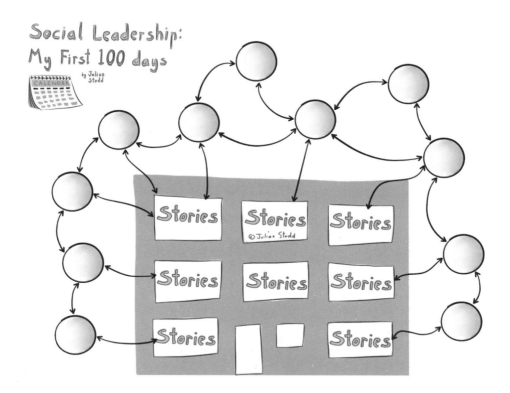

DAY 20: WHERE ARE THE STORIES?

Think about your organisation. How does it use stories? These might be adverts, internal communication or complex programme objectives. List ten places where stories are used within your organisation:

1. _____

2. _____

3. _____

4. _____

5. _____

6. _____

7. _____

8. _____

9. _____

10. _____

Ask some people around you: where do they see stories used?

Stories are the way that information flows around the organisation: we touch them every day. Some flow across in plain sight, whilst other are hidden. Some last for many years, whilst others are disposable.

Social Leadership:
My First 100 days

CALENDAR
by Julian Stodd

Formal
© Julian Stodd

Or Social ?

DAY 21: FORMAL OR SOCIAL?

Look back at yesterday's entry, where you listed where stories sit within the organisation: go back and write next to each one whether that story is '*formal*' or '*social*'.

A '*formal*' story is one that is written and owned by the organisation, whilst a 'social' story is one that is written and owned by us, the community.

How many were formal? _____

How many were social? _____

How does the balance look? Do you think you've captured them all, or are there stories that are hidden to you? Out of sight? Formal stories that the organisation hides from you (maybe for good reasons) and social stories that you're not party to?

Social Leaders are connected in many spaces, both formal and social. Their ability to hear and shape formal and socially co-created stories, as well as to help others shape their stories, is key to their success.

DAY 22: RESPONDING TO STORIES

Where are the spaces for people to respond to formal, organisational stories? When we hear these stories, we react to them: we may be inspired, annoyed or indifferent to them. Where can we share these feelings?

List some spaces where people can react to the formal organisational stories that they are subjected to:

1. _____

2. _____

3. _____

Is there enough space to respond?

Is there a consequence for those people who do respond?

Consequence can prevent people from responding to formal organisational stories.

Through the formal application of consequence, organisations can drown out the very curiosity and dissent that may be of most help to them as they make decisions.

We need all the stories, not just the ones we agree with.

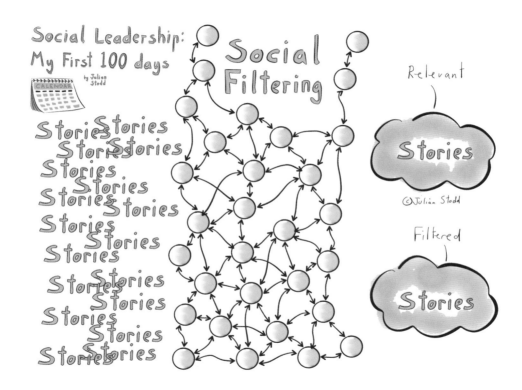

Social Leadership: My First 100 days
by Julian Stodd

Social Filtering

Stories Stories

Relevant
Stories
©Julian Stodd

Filtered
Stories

DAY 23: BRIDGING THE GAP

20-29
Storytelling

If we drive stories of dissent out of earshot, we are not silencing them: we are simply failing to learn from them.

How can you be a filter in this process? How, and where, can you hear feedback on formal stories? What can you do about it?

There is a process called Social Filtering: this is where the community hears all the stories, and figures out which ones are relevant. If you hear all the stories, and help figure out which are relevant, you are helping the organisation to become more Socially Dynamic.

Can you think of an example of a time when you have heard the 'noise' in the system, but felt unable to do anything with it? Unable to make sense of it?

This is the story I heard: _____

_____

_____

_____

_____

DAY 24: NARRATIVE AND STORY

The '*narrative*' of a story is the underlying information architecture, and the 'story' is the language that we put around it. You can tell many stories around one narrative track. For example, there have been several films about the sinking of the Titanic: they all share the same broad narrative, but each of the stories is different.

Sometimes we can help narratives to spread further by telling a new story on top of them, instead of simply forwarding on the original. We can make the story more relevant by adapting the language for the audience.

Have a go at it: write a story about how stories are used in your organisation. We have already discussed it here, but you can write your own story, in your own language. Our narrative is the same, but it will be your story.

My story: _____

_____

_____

_____

_____

_____

Social Leadership:
My First 100 days
by Julian Stodd

An

Action

Day

© Julian Stodd

DAY 25: AN ACTION DAY

Yesterday you wrote a story, a story explaining how stories are used within your organisation.

Was it any good? Perhaps. Or would it have been better if you had the feedback of your community?

Share your story into your community.

Where will you do this? _____

_____

_____

_____

If you have a blog, you could share it there.

You could publish it on LinkedIn.

You could just create an email group.

What would stop you from doing this? Are you comfortable with how you shape and share stories? If not, what can you learn from your discomfort? These are the very real challenges Social Leaders face: to build their own capability in storytelling, and to help others to build theirs.

Today is an action day: put aside the book and share your story.

Social Leadership:
My First 100 days
by Julian Stodd

Storytellers weave a Story of difference and Similarity

© Julian Stodd

DAY 26: CHARTING DIFFERENCE

In organisational life, we often seek consensus, but in social spaces, we can hold multiple different views. One role of the Social Leader is to be a storyteller for the group, to help the group co-create its story.

Part of this is to document what we agree on, and where our differences are. So the story we write is like the story a journalist would write: observing, evidencing, adding commentary.

By doing this, we are not reinforcing either opinion, but rather we are helping the community in its 'sense-making' activity, by clearly laying out what we see in the conversations.

In which space could you take on this role? Is it a project community, a strategy group, or something else?

I can be the storyteller for this community: _____

_____

_____

If you feel confident, give it a go now: write your first story charting difference and commonality.

Social Leadership:
My First 100 days
by Julian Stodd

©Julian Stodd

DAY 27: TYPES OF STORY

On Day 14 we looked at the different types of story we engage with: podcasts, videos, articles, images, etc.

Now consider which media you use to share stories. Rate these with a percentage:

1. Video _____

2. Text _____

3. Illustration _____

4. Audio _____

5. Other (please specify) _____

Are you limited to one medium of storytelling? How does that relate to the media that others use around you? What about the medium you consume most often: is it the same as the type you use yourself, or different?

What is the primary reason you don't feel confident or able to experiment with new approaches to storytelling? Share your reflections on the following:

1. Lack of time _____

2. Risk of failure _____

3. Not understanding how it works _____

4. Not sure of the value _____

Challenge yourself to try a new approach to storytelling.

DAY 28: LENGTH OF STORIES

What stories do you engage with every day, on news channels, on internal forums, through email, etc.?

Here are three stories I engage with every day:

1. _____

_____

2. _____

_____

3. _____

_____

How long are those stories?

Look at a story you have shared – perhaps an email or a report to a group.

Does the length of your story align with the length of the stories that you consume most often? Is it longer or shorter?

Would you consider rewriting your story as a result of this reflection?

Often we make our stories too long: people rarely complain about short stories. Organisations rarely tell them.

DAY 29: THE BEST STORYTELLER

Who is the best storyteller you know in your organisation, or in one of your communities?

Write them an email to tell them that, and to explain why you have chosen them.

The person is: _____

The reason I chose them is: _____

_____

_____

_____

Ask a few other people what they think: do you all agree on the same person? If not, what were their reasons?

© Julian Stodd

DAYS 30 TO 39: SHARING

Social Leaders shape great stories, but they don't add noise to a busy world: they share wisely, not just widely.

Consider what you share and how you share it: are you adding clarity or pollution to the system?

Social Leadership:
My First 100 days
by Julian Stodd

DAY 30: SIGNAL OR NOISE?

Take a look at what someone has shared with you: is it adding value, or is it just noise?

The signal is valuable, but the noise around it is not: it's the static in the system, obscuring and cluttering the channel.

What have they shared? _____

_____

_____

Is it signal ☐ or noise ☐ ?

What makes it 'signal' or 'noise'? _____

_____

_____

Organisations often obfuscate their own communication by adding too many words, too much 'fluff', too much extraneous information.

Individuals often pollute their own communication with irrelevant content (not aligned with the space they have curated), or material shared with many, but relevant to just a few.

Social Leaders share widely, but wisely.

Social Leadership:
My First 100 days
by Julian Stodd

Who Brings Clarity?

©Julian Stodd

DAY 31: CLARITY

Who shares the best content with you? _____

Were you able to identify one person, or was it a range of people? The question still stands: what do you engage with?

Why do you think it's so good? _____

DAY 32: ONE FOR ALL! BUT ALL FOR ONE?

Unlike the Three Musketeers, for whom everything was deemed to be shared with everyone, Social Leaders add value, not noise. Look back at the last group email you sent: did everyone need to be on it, or were you simply 'playing it safe', or even being lazy?

Maybe your communications are already highly specific, highly targeted, or maybe you could do better.

Can you identify an example of where you have shared wisely?

_____

_____

_____

_____

Can you identify an example of where you simply added to the noise?

_____

_____

_____

_____

The thing about our reputation is that it's built over time: we have to be consistent in adding value. If not, we are just clouding the waters.

Social Leadership:
My First 100 days
by Julian Stodd

NOiSE

© Julian Stodd

DAY 33: ESCAPING THE NOISE

Are you on a distribution list, a mailing list, a notification setting, that simply adds to your own noise? Are you putting off disengaging because inactivity is the easiest part? It may only take you a second to delete an email, or ignore a popular notification, but now's the time to clean up.

Spot some items in your inbox that are noise: go and unsubscribe or turn off notifications.

How many things can you clear out? _____

_____

_____

_____

DAY 34: INTERPRETATION

Part of ensuring that what we share adds value is interpreting it to be relevant for the audience: this process of interpretation is a storytelling exercise. '*I'm sharing this with you because…*'. The way we interpret the same content for different people may require a different context.

Again: Social Leaders share wisely. They may share something with three people, but with a personalised and individualised context, rather than a group email saying '*for interest*'.

What makes something relevant to you? What would be a good '*interpretation*' to add context if something was being shared with you? For me, it might be '*timely*', relating to current research. See if you can list three things that make something relevant:

1. _____

2. _____

3. _____

Strengthening our community is about adding value in depth, forging shared experiences and being generous with our expertise and time. Not just making the space noisy.

Social Leadership:
My First 100 days
by Julian Stodd

An Action Day

© Julian Stodd

DAY 35: AN ACTION DAY

Find an article that is of interest to your industry, perhaps something future facing, talking about how others are adapting, or an innovation. Write a line or two to interpret it to be relevant for two of your contacts or communities. Share it and see what happens.

These are the two places I shared it: _____

_____

_____

This is the response I got: _____

_____

_____

This is what I found: _____

_____

_____

This is how I interpreted it: _____

_____

_____

Social Leadership:
My First 100 days
by Julian Stodd

Thank You
© Julian Stodd

DAY 36: RECIPROCATING

Did you get a response to the story you wrote and shared yesterday? If you did, what format did it take? If not, have you thought why not?

How do you respond when people share with you?

Do you just consume the content? Do you share it directly, or add a new context around it? Do you say '*thank you*'?

Look back at the last few things that people have shared with you. How did you respond?

Now that you are taking some reflective time, are you happy with how you responded, or is there something you could have done differently?

.

These are my three examples:

1. _____

2. _____

3. _____

I could have done this differently: _____

_____

_____

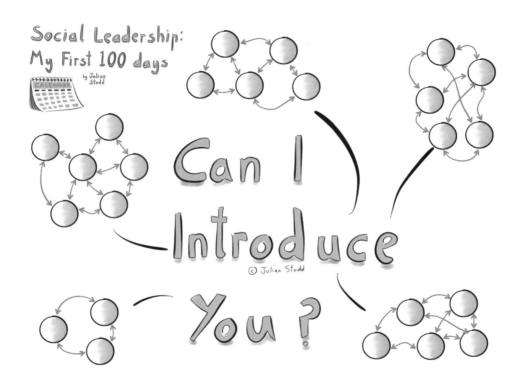

Social Leadership:
My First 100 days
by Julian Stodd

Can I Introduce You?

© Julian Stodd

DAY 37: SHARING COMMUNITY

Social Leaders help others to be successful, sometimes by sharing access and connections. Which community are you in that you think is particularly useful: a place where you have great conversations, where you discover new information or ways of working, a community that supports you?

It doesn't have to be a face-to-face community: maybe it's a TwitterChat group, or even a mailing group.

Can you think of someone who would benefit from this? Can you introduce them?

The community I am thinking of is: _____

_____

_____

The person I will introduce is: _____

_____

_____

It may only be a small action, but generosity is made up of small signs and footsteps.

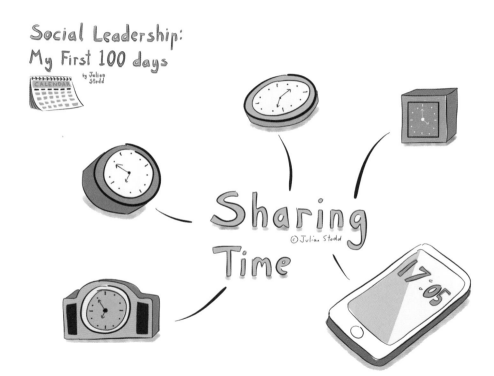

Social Leadership:
My First 100 days
by Julian Stodd

Sharing
Time
© Julian Stodd

DAY 38: SHARING TIME

It's time to share some time again. Who can you share it with, and what can you help them do?

I can help this person: _____

_____

_____

With this thing: _____

_____

_____

Why did you choose that person? Have they been generous to you in the past? Are they a friend, or a colleague?

We have some people in our networks with whom we share strong 'social ties', people with whom we have shared experiences and time.

Is there someone you know less well? Who can you reach out to, with an offer of support, who you don't know so well?

Effective Social Leaders will maintain larger numbers of broad social ties: some people they know well, who may be friends, but also others who they are helping to succeed.

30-39
Sharing

Social Leadership:
My First 100 days
by Julian Stodd

Sharing
© Julian Stodd

Uncertainty

DAY 39: SHARING UNCERTAINTY

We don't always have to show or project strength: it's OK to ask for help too, to share our uncertainties.

Is there something you don't know how to do well: a particular system, a particular process, how to do something in a piece of software? Who can you share that uncertainty with?

The thing I am uncertain about is: _____

_____

The person I will share this with is: _____

_____

How does it feel to share uncertainty?

It feels:
[FOOLISH] ☐   [AWKWARD] ☐
[EMBARRASSING] ☐   [NORMAL] ☐
[SAFE] ☐   [RISKY] ☐
or something else?

_____

_____

Perhaps you feel strong and able to share your uncertainty, or perhaps it makes you vulnerable? Great Social Leaders anticipate these feelings in others, and do what they can to welcome the sharing of uncertainty.

30-39
Sharing

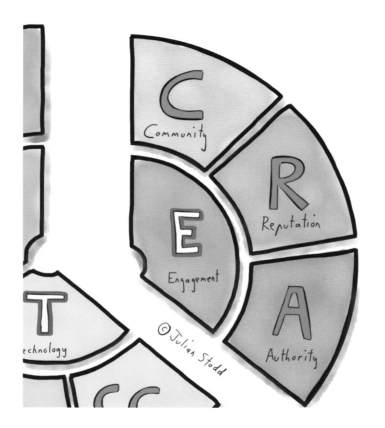

ENGAGEMENT: FIND YOUR VOICE, INHABIT THE SPACES, BECOME A SOCIAL LEADER

In '*Engagement*', we will consider how you are engaged in your communities: where these communities are, the role you take within them, how you earn your reputation, and how that reputation leads to your Social Authority.

When we were looking at Narrative, we were thinking about choosing a space, taking a stance, and curating our voice and presence around that. We thought about how we shaped and shared our stories, and how those stories spread.

Now we are outward facing, considering the way we want to be in the world, and how we earn our reputation.

Social Leaders are deeply engaged: they exist in many different communities and their reputation is founded upon a humility of engagement. They do not seek to lead with force and formal power, but rather through fairness, trust and authentic action.

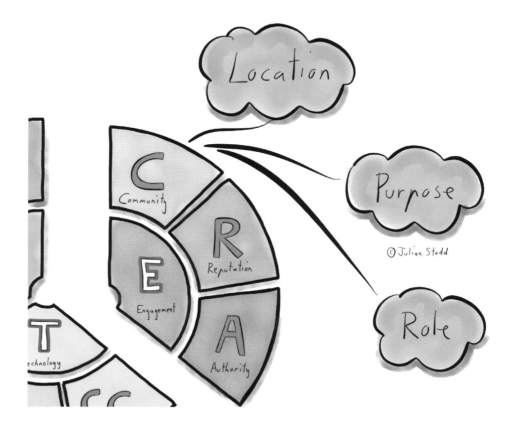

© Julian Stodd

DAYS 40 TO 49: COMMUNITY

A community is much more than just a collection of people: it shares values and purpose. We belong to many different communities, some highly formal, others deeply social. In some we are central, in others we are but bystanders.

Mastering community, how it works, how it forms, how it finds its coherence and energy, this is what Social Leaders do, because they recognise that *'community'* is where their reputation and Social Authority resides.

Social Leadership:
My First 100 days
by Julian Stodd

Where
are your
© Julian Stodd
Communities ?

DAY 40: WHERE ARE YOUR COMMUNITIES?

We are connected to many people in many different ways. Think about people who you are connected to in person, the people you see day by day, week by week, or just a few times a year. What are those communities?

For example: sports teams, leadership teams, friends you meet for brunch, professional conferences.

Can you list ten communities like this?

1. _____

2. _____

3. _____

4. _____

5. _____

6. _____

7. _____

8. _____

9. _____

10. _____

40-49
Community

These are the communities into which we have direct links. We know what people look like, we understand how formal or social the groupings are. These are our foundation communities.

DAY 41: WHERE ARE YOUR OTHER COMMUNITIES?

Some of our communities are virtual, online, distant: we do not share physical spaces, we may not even have met in person.

For example: specific forums online, Twitter communities, remote project teams.

Can you name ten of these?

1. _____

2. _____

3. _____

4. _____

5. _____

6. _____

7. _____

8. _____

9. _____

10. _____

Was it easy to list ten, or a struggle? You may have listed 20 communities by this stage: ten online and ten in the physical world. Can you spot differences between the two?

40-49
Community

Social Leadership:
My First 100 days
by Julian Stodd

Leave

Join

Build

Communities

© Julian Stodd

DAY 42: COMING AND GOING

There are three things to consider. Which of these communities add value (or do you add value to), and you will stay in? Which existing communities have run their course, and you can leave? And which new communities should you be trying to join or build?

For example, you may be connected to a community from a previous job, a previous company, a previous project. Sure, you may stay connected to certain people as friends, but are you active in the community itself? Are you sharing, are you supporting, are you engaged?

If not, is it time to leave?

You can't do everything. One thing we know for sure about the Social Age is that it's full of distractions: a casual glimpse tells me that I'm a 'member' of more than 40 LinkedIn groups, but if I'm honest, I neither contribute to nor consume stories from many of them in any meaningful way. I could probably reduce the 'noise' in my system by leaving.

Similarly, I may not be in the right communities for current interests or work.

Which community could you safely leave? _____

_____

Which community do you need to find? _____

_____

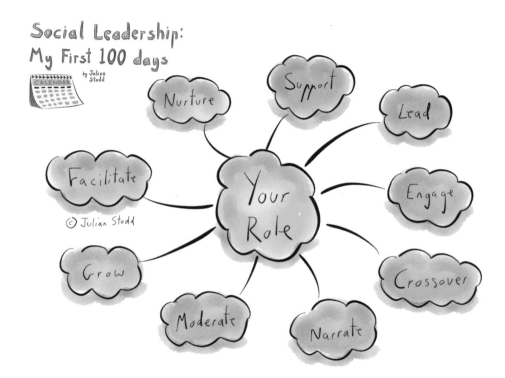

DAY 43: YOUR ROLE

We take different roles within our communities. Sometimes we lead, sometimes we are there for enlightenment, sometimes we are just there for interest or amusement. Sometimes there is a certain status from being within a community. Which communities are you in for these reasons?

In which community do you take a leadership role?

_____

In which community do you learn the most?

_____

Which community gives you the most support?

_____

In which community do you support the most people?

_____

In which community do you most enjoy being?

_____

Which community frustrates you most often?

_____

Is there a bias? Do you consume more than you share? Or share more than you consume?

_____

Social Leaders often put aside the mantle of leadership when they are within communities: they seek to help others to succeed, through a generosity of time, attitude and effort.

Social Leadership:
My First 100 days
by Julian Stodd

In the
arms of
Community

© Julian Stodd

DAY 44: THE ARMS OF COMMUNITY

Pick one of your communities, for example, a project team.

Pick three people in that community. What are they known for? What is their reputation?

The first person is: _____

I know them for: _____

_____

Does it feel comfortable to write this? Do you think they know what their reputation is?

Are you hedging your bets and choosing people with good reputations?

The second person is: _____

I know them for: _____

_____

Would you say this to someone's face? Do you think they know what you would say?

The third person is you.

What is your reputation? _____

What are you known for? _____

_____

40-49
Community

Social Leadership:
My First 100 days
by Julian Stodd

An Action Day

© Julian Stodd

DAY 45: AN ACTION DAY

It's an action day: go and find a new community to which you can contribute.

Not sure where to start?

Ask in your other communities. Ask people you respect, as people you know.

What community will you join? _____

_____

Why have you chosen this? _____

_____

Do you feel too busy? Have you left enough communities?

If being within a community feels like hard work, it may not be right for you. Remember, you can stay friends with people, but you don't have to be an active member of a community with them.

40-49
Community

DAY 46: STARTING COMMUNITIES

Is there something you need help with? Is there something you are good at that you could help others with? Is there something you think your organisation needs to address, but there is no forum in which to address it?

Take competition: is there a community where you can discuss effective competition? What do you see happening out in the world, and how can you, and your organisation, learn from it? Everyone knows about Uber, about ZAPOS, about Airbnb, about how successful they are, about how disruptive they are, but is your organisation learning from them?

You could start a community to explore how other organisations are effective competitors. Or how they are agile. Or how they recruit. Or how they manage change.

Perhaps other people share your curiosity? Why not create the space to explore?

Remember: if it doesn't work, you can stop it, you can leave it, you can disband it or hand it on. Communities are not permanent. Nor is our role within them.

What community can you start? _____

_____

DAY 47: PROFESSIONAL COMMUNITIES

There are many professional communities, ones that bring together people with similar roles or interests. Are you a member of any professional communities? Perhaps it is an accrediting body, or perhaps it runs annual conferences and speaking events?

Look at your list of communities: would you classify any of them as 'professional communities'?

Yes ☐

No ☐

If 'yes', what is the primary thing you take away from your membership? Is it status, new information or camaraderie, and do you take a lot or a little? Should you be staying in this community, or looking for a better one?

If you answered 'no', do you know which communities you could join? Ask around your colleagues and network and see which ones they are in.

Social Leadership:
My First 100 days
by Julian Stodd

Dissent

Agreement

Confirmation

Echoes

Where will I hear new Voices?

Fresh

Challenge

Context

Perspective

40-49
Community

DAY 48: BIAS IN COMMUNITIES

We tend to have a bias in our views, not because we We tend to have a bias in our views, not because we are not connected to many people, but because we are connected to many people who think like us, who do similar jobs to us.

Look at the communities that you are in: are they all related to a specific subject matter? For example, are many of them '*HR*' communities, or '*Engineering*' communities, or '*Social*' communities?

Try taking your list of communities, and categorising them: what do you notice?

This is what I notice: _____

_____

We can broaden our worldview by joining some new communities in spaces where we are light: for example, a good independent news community, or a generic 'organisational change' community. Perhaps an alumni group from our old university?

The trick here is to consider '*where do I hear voices that agree with me, and where will I hear new voices?*' We want to ensure that our communities contain both types of voice.

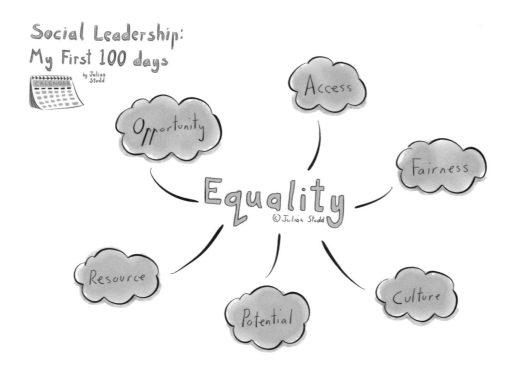

DAY 49: EQUALITY

Are the communities that you are in fair and equal? Take a look: are they representative of the wider world, or are they echo chambers of people from the same cultural and ethnic background as yourself?

What can you do about it if one of your communities is not diverse?

This is a tough question: is it our individual responsibility to drive for greater inclusion and diversity, or is it someone else's responsibility? Do people not join certain communities because they are just '*not for them*'?

As Social Leaders, it's our responsibility to address this. If your communities feel diverse and inclusive, you are lucky. If not, what can you do? Start by talking to one person about this, because change starts with small steps.

Who can you talk to? _____

_____

In which community are they? _____

_____

What did you talk about? _____

_____

_____

_____

40-49
Community

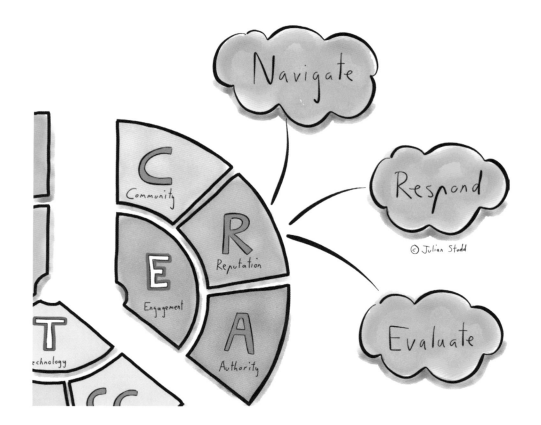

© Julian Stodd

DAYS 50 TO 59: REPUTATION

Through their actions, Social Leaders earn their reputation within their communities. Authentic action earns reputation: not simply being part of a system, but helping to make the system better. Social Leadership is not a passive role: it's an active journey.

Reputation is not bestowed by the organisation, nor is it represented by position within a hierarchy: it cannot be bought and it cannot be demanded.

If we act with humility, with fairness, with kindness, with respect, we may be awarded a reputation. Within this framework for developing Social Leadership, we seek to curate a space and earn our reputation within an area that we are conscious of. We are not trying to control it, but rather to mindfully earn it.

True social reputation is resilient: our community will forgive us our mistakes and errors if those are against a backdrop of openness, fairness and a willingness to learn. Nobody is perfect.

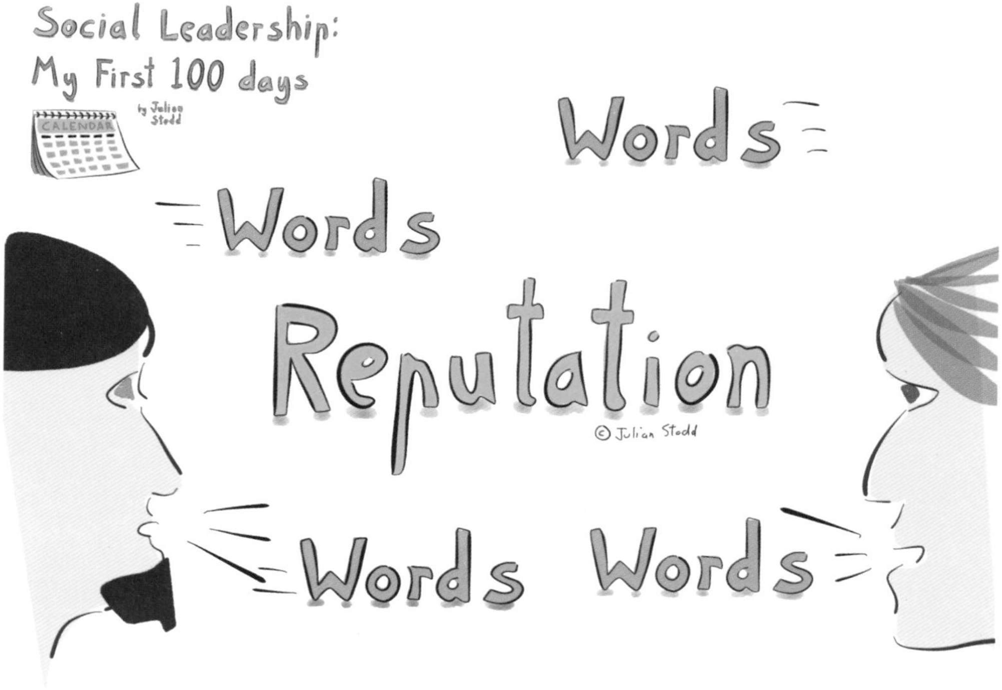
Social Leadership:
My First 100 days
CALENDAR
by Julian Stodd
Words
Words
Reputation
© Julian Stodd
Words
Words

DAY 50: WHAT IS YOUR REPUTATION?

Do you know what you are known for? How would people describe you? What do they think your strengths and weaknesses are?

Ask two people to talk about reputation: what do they know you for?

Ask them to give you three words each.

The first person I asked said: 1. _____

2. _____   3. _____

The second person I asked said: 1. _____

2. _____   3. _____

Was this what you expected? Were the words they used the same or different? How do you feel about what they said?

I feel: _____

_____

_____

_____

_____

DAY 51: KNOW YOURSELF

When we talked about curation earlier, we chose a space. What three words would you use to describe your ideal reputation? What would you like to be known for?

I would like to be known for these three things:

1. _____   2. _____

3. _____

Are these the same things that people told you, or are there differences? What do those differences mean?

Reflecting on the words you use, and the words others used, how do you feel?

I feel:

_____

_____

Our reputation is contextual and varied: some people will know us for one thing, others for something else. But there are foundations: it's these foundations that we are focused on.

Reputation is not made in the moment, it's earned over time.

50-59
Reputation

DAY 52: LOOK AROUND

Choose three people you work with who you admire.

What is their reputation? Again, choose three words for each.

The first person is: 1. _____

2. _____ 3. _____

The second person is: 1. _____

2. _____ 3. _____

The third person is: 1. _____

2. _____ 3. _____

Do you spot patterns? Are you attracted to certain trends? Or are they diverse? Is there a crossover with the words that you used to describe your own ideal reputation, or with the words that others used about you?

We tend to form teams in our own likeness, but strong teams have a diversified strength. In the context of Social Leadership, there is no one 'ideal' reputation, but rather a recognition that reputation is earned, not written in stone, that is it fluid and painted onto us by others.

50-59
Reputation

DAY 53: WORK IN PROGRESS

Chances are that when people gave you their three words to describe your reputation, they were positive. Chances are that you used three words yourself that were positive too. But what if you focus on areas where you could develop?

What three aspects of your reputation would you change, if you were really honest? Can you think of three words that people might sometimes use to describe you that reflect your weaker areas?

For example, people sometimes perceive me as being a bit opinionated. Sometimes I don't take enough time to listen to other people before expressing an opinion. I'm not terrible at it, but I could be more mindful.

What would be your three words or areas to consider?

The first aspect of my reputation I could reflect on is:

_____

The second is: _____

The third is: _____

This is not about rewiring your personality or building your perfect self: it's about mindfulness, about understanding all aspects of your reputation. By being more aware, we can be more attuned.

We are all works in progress: part of being a great leader is to understand your weaknesses, even if you can't change them.

50-59
Reputation

Social Leadership:
My First 100 days
by Julian Stodd

Habit

Efficient
Unconscious
Residual
Limiting
Infectious
Static

©Julian Stodd

DAY 54: HABIT

Habits are powerful things: they are cognitively effective ways of responding to a situation, but are also sometimes things that trap us in ways of being in the world.

Part of understanding our reputation is to understand how habits can trap us: they reinforce our ways of reacting and hence, reinforce our reputation.

Be mindful of habits: can you identify three habits that you have?

For example, I know I am always very last minute in organising travel, which causes stress in others. It probably forms part of my reputation.

My first habit is: _____

_____

My second habit is: _____

_____

Another habit I have is: _____

_____

If you had to work on one of these, which would it be?

I would work on: _____

_____

The first step is to be conscious and mindful of a habit: that way, it's in our spotlight, and we can change it!

Social Leadership:
My First 100 days
by Julian Stodd

An Action Day

© Julian Stodd

DAY 55: AN ACTION DAY

Today is an action day! We have thought so far about our own habits and reputation: what about others?

Social Leaders help others to be successful, and sometimes to do that they have to be brave, as well as generous with their time and energy.

Who have you identified who has a reputation that is not as strong as it could be? What could you do to help them? For example, is there someone who always presents shabby documents, or who is constantly late? How can you help them to improve?

Maybe you can simply talk to them about reputation. After all, you are engaged in an exercise to be mindful about their own reputation, perhaps they would value thinking about theirs?

Unless you are one of the few people who could find no rough corners on your reputation, chances are that you work with other imperfect people.

Being mindful is about a willingness to talk about it. Talk to someone about reputation, yours and theirs.

The person I talked to is: _____

We talked about: _____

_____

_____

Afterwards, this is what I thought: _____

_____

I hope today has been slightly challenging: facing our own development is never easy. But if we feel thoughtful afterwards, it's worth it. Perhaps we can earn a reputation for reflection.

50-59
Reputation

Social Leadership:
My First 100 days
by Julian Stodd

CALENDAR

Authenticity

DAY 56: AUTHENTICITY

Our ability to engage effectively in social spaces is linked to the authenticity of our stories and actions: it's a factor that impacts directly on reputation.

What does '*authenticity*' mean to you? _____

_____

_____

_____

We will each understand it differently, but often there is something about alignment to core values: if we act in line with our values, and those of our community, we are deemed authentic.

It's a feature of organisational life that sometimes we have to compromise: we have to do things that we are not comfortable with, but which need to be done.

Can you identify an example of where you have had to compromise your authenticity due to a particular challenge or constraint at work?

Perhaps you are involved in restructuring, but unable to tell a friend that their job is at risk. These are impossible situations, but ever more likely as formal and social worlds collide.

However hard it might be, striving to be authentic to our core values is core to Social Leadership.

DAY 57: IMPACT

Of course, the pressure of organisational life does not just impact on us, it impacts on others. Ask three people about what authenticity means to them. Get them to give you three words each.

The first person I asked said: 1. _____

2. _____ 3. _____

The second person said this: 1. _____

2. _____ 3. _____

The last person chose these three words:

1. _____ 2. _____

3. _____

Were they the same words as you chose, or different?

How many of these words apply to you?

I can relate most to these three words: 1. _____

2. _____ 3. _____

Which one word out of all them would you most want to be used to describe your reputation?

_____

_____

50-59
Reputation

DAY 58: THANK YOU

Simple things can impact our reputation: the courtesy of saying '*thank you*', or of recognising and rewarding people with respect.

Is there someone in one of your communities that you feel strives hard, someone who tries to add value? Can you give them some respect? Why not call it out? Thank them, and explain why.

The person I want to thank is: _____

_____

_____

Their reputation is: _____

_____

_____

The response I got was: _____

_____

_____

Perhaps this was easy to do: perhaps your organisation has a thankful culture, one where it is common to award recognition and respect.

Many people do not operate in that space: they are too 'busy', or the culture would deem it weird to offer public thanks and recognition. But social recognition powers social systems.

We will have the culture that we create: do your part to normalise thanks and to help others to build their reputation.

DAY 59: CALL IT OUT

We've spent ten days talking about '*reputation*'. So call it: what one thing will you try to work on going forward?

The thing I will work on is: _____

_____

Are you brave enough to ask someone for help with this? If so, who?

_____

_____

How did they respond to your asking for help?

_____

_____

If we change nothing, nothing will change. We can look forever at the faults of others, but only by starting with our own faults can we change the culture.

© Julian Stodd

60-69
Authority

DAYS 60 TO 69: AUTHORITY

As we earn our reputation, through our actions, we may be awarded Social Authority: it's our power, the power granted to us, contextually, consensually, by those who surround us.

Formal authority is given to us by the organisation: it's held within hierarchies, captured in organisational charts and contracts, sanctioned through orders and edicts – and it carries the weight of reprimand behind it.

Social Authority, by contrast, is a magnetic form of power: it's the power to lead others through consent, through partnership, through bonds of trust and fairness. You can have all the formal power in the world, and yet lack Social Authority. Or you can have high Social Authority, and yet hold no formal position of power at all. That's the strange thing about Social Leadership: it's power beyond the system, power outside the system.

With our Social Authority comes responsibility: the community that gives it to us may take it away again.

You cannot ask for or demand Social Authority: you cannot buy it or steal it. You can only be given it.

60-69
Authority

Social Leadership:
My First 100 days

by Julian Stodd

Helping

©Julian Stodd

Hands

60-69
Authority

DAY 60: A HELPING HAND

Can you think of a time when you got something done through the help of others? Chances are, there are many times. I can think of a few, from the time when friends helped me to get a sofa up the stairs, to a time when I put on a community conference, without a budget, simply through the support of others.

Give an example of a time when you were successful through the support of others:

_____

_____

_____

_____

Why did they help you? _____

_____

_____

We are rarely effective simply through the application of formal power: most often, there is an element of goodwill, something extra involved, at least at some point. Sometimes, we would be utterly unable to be effective without it.

Social Leadership:
My First 100 days
by Julian Stodd

Inspir♥tion

© Julian Stodd

DAY 61: WHO ARE YOU INSPIRED TO HELP?

To follow up: who do you invest Social Authority in? Who has earned a reputation where you would follow them, where you would help them?

Give an example of when you have stepped up to support someone, be it to help them on a project, to get a job, or to deal with a crisis.

What is your example? _____

_____

_____

Why did you help them? _____

_____

_____

The chances are that you would not have invested this effort equally: some people have earned your respect, your friendship, your trust, whilst others have not.

It's not necessarily that you dislike or mistrust them: they may simply have not invested anything in the relationship. There is simply ambiguity, simply no reason to help them.

This is where Social Leaders expend energy: in consciously curating their space and humbly earning their reputation, recognising that this will sit at the heart of their Social Authority.

60-69
Authority

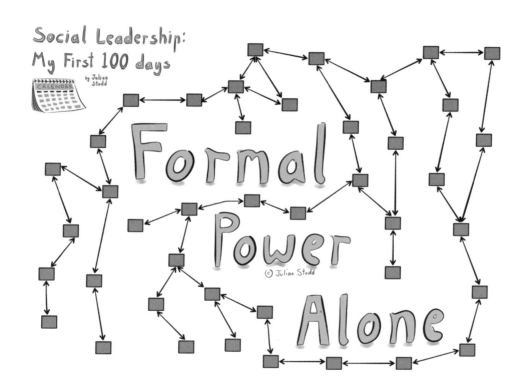

DAY 62: FORMAL POWER ALONE

List five things that you can only achieve through formal authority.

1. The first thing is: _____

2. The second thing is: _____

3. The third thing is: _____

4. The fourth thing is: _____

5. The final thing is: _____

Do these things have anything in common? For example, do they all cost money? Or do they all involve significant infra-structure? Or specific qualifications? Or political access?

Can you identify any trends in your answers?

The examples I chose have these three traits in common:

1. _____

2. _____

3. _____

Was it easy or hard to spot trends?

60-69
Authority

Social Leadership:
My First 100 days
by Julian Stodd

Social
Power
Alone

(c) Julian Stodd

DAY 63: SOCIAL POWER ALONE

List five things you can only achieve through Social Authority, the support and power of your community:

1. The first thing is: _____

2. The second thing is: _____

3. The third thing is: _____

4. The fourth thing is: _____

5. The final thing is: _____

Did these things have anything in common? Are they related to communities and crowds, or technology and engineering? Are they generally large things or small things?

Chances are that the answers you gave yesterday and today are unique to you, but it's good to spot trends. Can you spot any so far?

Generally my formal authority is useful when: _____

And my Social Authority is vital when: _____

60-69
Authority

Social Leadership:
My First 100 days
by Julian Stodd

When Social Authority FAILS.

© Julian Stodd

DAY 64: FAILURE

Social Authority is just another type of power: it's not that it's inherently good or bad, it's just power awarded through the community.

Unfortunately, that means that some people use their Social Authority for the wrong things: they build influence within certain communities and are empowered to make their space less fair, less equal.

Any community has its differences, but at the heart of Social Leadership is the fight for fairness, for equality, to be kind and humble.

Where do you see failures of Social Authority? Can you give an example?

_____

_____

Talk to someone else about this. What is their example?

_____

_____

Was there any commonality between your two answers? Can you read anything into that? If you have an insight, share it here:

_____

_____

Don't worry if you don't: we are carrying out reflective activities, and sometimes we find answers, sometimes we don't. Those questions just carry forward with us. It's not always the answers that count: it's the fact we are willing to search for them.

60-69
Authority

Social Leadership:
My First 100 days
by Julian Stodd

An Action Day

© Julian Stodd

DAY 65: AN ACTION DAY

Explore your Social Authority: find a voice within the community.

Ask a question, something about how the organisation can improve, and see what response you get.

The question that I asked was: _____

_____

Did anyone answer? YES ☐ NO ☐

If 'yes', was it the people you expected who answered, or people you did not expect?

_____

_____

What surprised you about this experience? _____

_____

What reinforced your preconceptions? _____

_____

Regularly test your willingness to engage, regularly question yourself. This is part of how we get 'off the starting blocks' and move from 'intent' into 'action'.

60-69
Authority

DAY 66: CONTEXT

You can have high Social Authority in one context or community, and low Social Authority in another, unrelated one. Our communities can exist in total isolation of one another, so our reputation in one space may not flow through to another.

Can you think of one context in which you have high Social Authority, where your voice is heard loudly, not through your formal authority, but because your stories and tone of voice resonate?

My example of high Social Authority is: _____

_____

_____

Can you think of a context in which you have low or no Social Authority, where you have to exert your formal authority to get things done?

My example of low Social Authority is: _____

_____

_____

Can you draw any conclusions from this? Is there an obvious divide, or ambiguity? Because Social Leadership is contextual, it's often hard to definitively sense a divide: it's not as simple as having one type of authority, consistently, in one space.

60-69
Authority

DAY 67: RELATIONSHIP VS TRANSACTION

There is a difference between transactional activities and relationship ones: inevitably, Social Leadership is more about relationships, but there can be a transactional component too. Wise transacting can be an example of how we support each other.

The key thing is that there is never an expectation of reciprocity for Social Leaders: they help in order to help others, they strive for what is right because it is right, not for the reward.

Name one thing you regularly do that is transactional:

_____

_____

And one thing that is based on relationships: _____

_____

Can you identify an example where you have moved from one space to the other, where you have initiated the change, for example, from transactional to relationship?

_____

_____

Our ability to deploy the right type of power in the right context is important: there is a time and a place for formal authority, but often our Social Authority will be enough, if we work to earn it. And if we earn it, it can run far deeper than formal authority.

DAY 68: AMPLIFICATION

Our Social Authority correlates to the amplification of our stories and hence, our influence and power within our communities.

What causes stories to be amplified? List five things:

1. _____

2. _____

3. _____

4. _____

5. _____

We've already talked about how stories work, how they are shared. If we have developed our storytelling ability, we should feel the effects of amplification. Reputation, plus great storytelling, leads to stronger Social Authority.

60-69
Authority

Social Leadership:
My First 100 days
by Julian Stodd

Great
Storytelling
© Julian Stodd

Authenticity

DAY 69: AUTHENTICITY

We've mentioned 'authenticity' before: it's the foundation of great storytelling and hence, Social Authority.

Think of a great Social Leader, perhaps a famous figure, a colleague or a friend.

How authentic are they? Can you characterise their reputation in three words?

The first person I can think of with high authenticity is

_____ ,

and their reputation is based upon _____ ,

_____ ,

and _____ .

How authentic do you think you are to others?

NOT VERY ☐   SOMEWHAT ☐   VERY ☐

What will you do about this? _____

_____

60-69
Authority

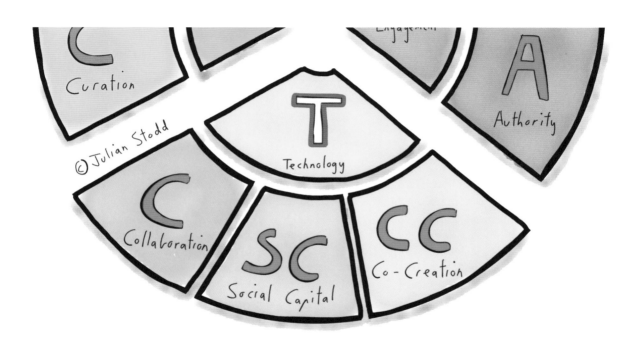

© Julian Stodd

TECHNOLOGY: USE THE SPACE TO CO-CREATE, DEVELOP OTHERS, CLOSE THE CIRCLE

We come to the final third of the NET Model, 'Technology', where we surface and celebrate those things that only reputation and Social Authority can give us. With a strong reputation and awarded authority, we can co-create new knowledge and solutions within our communities. We will have developed high Social Capital and be able to use it to instil it in others. And we will collaborate widely and effectively.

There is nothing particularly special about Social Leadership: it's just a more dynamic and fluid type of power. It's based upon a reflection of how we are in the world, of how we, and others, perceive us, and of the ways that we can impact that through our actions.

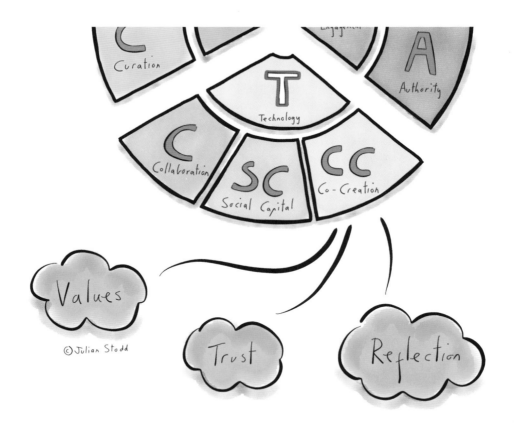

©Julian Stodd

DAYS 70 TO 79: CO-CREATION

Co-creation is the magic that happens within our high-functioning communities. It emerges when people bring their skills, their knowledge, their understanding and empathy, their capability and their cognitive surplus. It's a discussion, prototyping, and storytelling activity.

As Social Leaders, we want our communities to be great 'sense-making' entities, great at co-creating learning, co-creating change, co-creating meaning out of the noise.

DAY 70: IMPETUS, INCENTIVE, MOMENTUM

High-functioning communities are dynamic co-creative spaces. They can give us impetus and tempo in our work.

Think of these three words. For each, write your thoughts, including which is most important:

1. Impetus – Why would people engage in co-creation?

_____

_____

2. Incentive – What do people want out of it?

_____

_____

3. Momentum – What causes us to gain it, and what drains it?

_____

_____

70-79
Co-Creation

Social Leadership:
My First 100 days
by Julian Stodd

CALENDAR

Investing
in
Co-Creation

© Julian Stodd

DAY 71: MOTIVATION

Why would people invest their energy and time in co-creating solutions within communities? The answers are complex: for some, it's a chance to demonstrate expertise, for others, a chance to help. Some people enjoy the challenge, others are excited to make a difference.

What are your reasons for engaging in conversations within your communities?

My first reason is: _____

_____

My second reason is: _____

_____

My third reason is: _____

_____

Talk to two other people about what motivates them to engage: are their answers the same as yours, or can you spot differences?

Think about what causes you to engage, and whether you provide the same opportunities or rewards as those you look for from others.

70-79
Co-Creation

Social Leadership:
My First 100 days
by Julian Stodd

Who Owns the Conversation

© Julian Stodd

70-79
Co-Creation

DAY 72: OWNERSHIP

Who owns the co-created conversation? Ownership is important: if people help you solve something, or introduce you to new ideas, then you are in it together, but is everyone an equal owner?

For this to be fair, we have to consider the ownership of the space (the technology), and the ownership of the conversation (what we do on the technology).

It's possible that the organisation owns the technology on which the conversation takes place, but that doesn't mean that it owns the conversation. Conversations are fluid, and move between different spaces.

We can learn a lot from open-source software: the code is free to use and enjoy, but with it comes an obligation to the community to continue to develop and share back again.

What are your thoughts on the ownership of the conversation? You and I don't have to agree on this, but it's important that you are clear, and can clearly share your view.

This is what I think about ownership: _____

_____

_____

_____

70-79
Co-Creation

Social Leadership:
My First 100 days
by Julian Stodd

Reward

(c) Julian Stodd

DAY 73: REWARD

If people are helping us, and our organisations, to do better, we should reward them. But these are social spaces: we cannot use formal rewards, or we will just make the space formal. We need social rewards. For example, if someone is great at helping the community to tell their story, consider how we can help them to be an even more successful social storyteller.

Pick three ways that we can socially reward someone:

The first way is this: _____

The second is this: _____

And finally, this: _____

And what wouldn't you do? What would make the reward formal?

I would not do this: _____ ,

because (share your reason): _____

_____

DAY 74: KNOWLEDGE BIAS

When we are looking at the health of our social communities, their ability to co-create, we can consider whether there is any bias around knowledge. For example, does everyone just quote *Harvard Business Review*, or share TED Talks?

If we draw upon the same sources, we will be hearing one voice, but by drawing on new areas, we hear many voices: diversity of thought, and style, is a strength.

What three spaces do you rarely use, but could try to use more? For example, I draw heavily upon *New Scientist* to stay abreast of current research, but never read *Scientific American*. I always go to the BBC for my news. Maybe I should try, now and then, to get a different perspective?

My top three spaces are:

1. _____

2. _____

3. _____

Does this surprise you when you see it written down?

70-79
Co-Creation

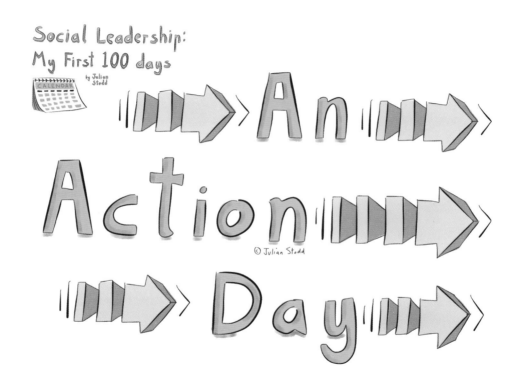

Social Leadership:
My First 100 days
by Julian Stodd

An Action Day

© Julian Stodd

DAY 75: AN ACTION DAY

It's an action day: put the book down and spend 30 minutes supporting people within your community. Look up an article to share with them (curation and storytelling activity), introduce them to new people (sharing activity), thank the people who have helped you recently (reputation activity – and just plain nice).

How did you feel at the end? You don't have to write '*happy*'. Maybe you felt too busy, or distracted, or frustrated. Document how it felt, honestly.

I felt: _____

_____

_____

_____

The way we feel when we engage is a key part of our motivation: if we feel too busy, foolish, or unsure, so will other people, and our community will not be very engaged.

If you live it, you can learn from it. We will come back to that when we discuss Social Capital in a few days' time.

70-79
Co-Creation

Social Leadership:
My First 100 days
by Julian Stodd

Co-Creative
POWER

Spend
Wisely

© Julian Stodd

DAY 76: BARRIERS

Ask three people for the top reason why they might not engage in co-creative activities within a community.

The first person said: _____

_____

The second person said: _____

_____

The third person said: _____

_____

Typically our engagement in social spaces relates to the relevance and timeliness of the conversation. Make sure that you are only inviting people to participate in conversations if you know that it's relevant for them.

Similarly, if you find your energy being spent on conversations that are not relevant to you, claim that time back.

Co-creation is the core of social communities, figuring things out. But our energy is limited and we must engage and spend it wisely.

70-79
Co-Creation

DAY 77: WHO ARE YOUR BEST FILTERS?

Whilst co-creation is the activity of a group, some people are '*noisier*' than others, whilst some people filter better. Can you think of someone who is a good filter?

How would you know? Because chances are that you give them airspace: if they share something, you will read it, if they ask for your time, you will give it.

Our ability to co-create will rely on our reputation and Social Authority, our ability to filter effectively and to build networks that include great filters: other Social Leaders.

Who do you know who filters effectively? _____

_____

What do they do that you could learn from? _____

_____

_____

70-79
Co-Creation

Social Leadership:
My First 100 days
by Julian Stodd

Our Shared Differences

© Julian Stodd

70-79
Co-Creation

DAY 78: CULTURAL DIFFERENCE

Globally, we are separated by distance, but also by moral, legal and ethical boundaries. In some countries homosexuality is illegal, in others it's simply an ordinary part of life. In some countries bribery is taboo, whilst in others, it's how business gets done.

Because technology allows us to connect with ease, we might assume that we connect as equals, but we don't. This underlying difference may lead to disempowerment, loss of voice, or direct conflict.

How do you think cultural difference may impact on our ability to co-create within communities?

These challenges won't be overcome through technology, nor through rules alone, because when everyone is operating within their local culture, they are experiencing what is viewed as '*normal*'. We cannot underestimate the challenges of cultural difference. The solution will surely lie in engagement with respect, not simply a naive assumption that rules will keep us safe.

70-79
Co-Creation

Social Leadership:
My First 100 days
by Julian Stodd

Voiceless

DAY 79: THE VOICELESS

List five ways in which people can be left without a voice, left outside the ability to co-create.

1. _____

2. _____

3. _____

4. _____

5. _____

And list one way in which you can address this, one way you can help them find a voice:

_____

_____

Your role as a Social Leader is to be effective, to co-create solutions to challenging problems, to be agile, to respond at speed. But also to help others to succeed: to be the voice for those who have none, to stand up for what is right, what is fair.

To be kind. To drive change. The 'co' in 'co-creation' means 'we', not 'me'.

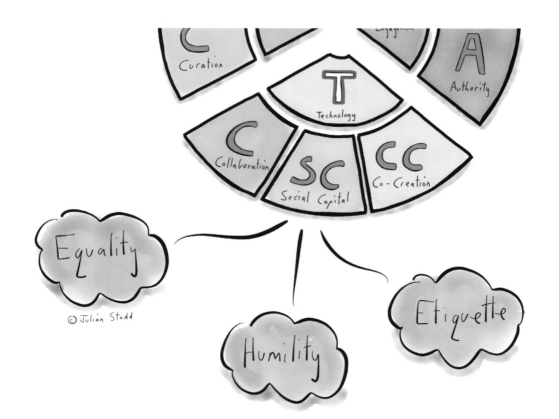

DAYS 80 TO 89: SOCIAL CAPITAL

With authority comes responsibility: a need to do what is right. Social Capital can be defined as our ability to '*survive and thrive*' in community spaces, and our ability to help others to do the same.

The very technology that permits and enhances collaboration can unintentionally disempower and inhibit, if we fail to safeguard, protect and nurture. That disenfranchisement can come through ignorance, active persecution, poverty, capability, or discrimination. As Social Leaders, we must fight all these things.

Communities are based upon shared values: we must find and live these.

80-89
Social Capital

Social Leadership:
My First 100 days
by Julian Stodd

Social Leaders do what's not just Right EASY

© Julian Stodd

DAY 80: DO WHAT'S RIGHT

Social Leaders must do what is right, even when that choice takes them into conflict with the formal system. Indeed, just 'following orders' is the very definition of a formal hierarchy dominating social conscience.

We need rules, we need systems, we need processes, but equally we need challenge and we need subversion, we need to be accountable, and we need to do what is right.

Think of an example, in your organisation or experience, where a formal system has done something wrong, something that has disenfranchised or disempowered someone, but where you have felt powerless, unwilling or unable to do anything about it.

The situation I can think of is: _____

_____

_____

_____

_____

_____

Talk this over with someone: how did they feel about it?

80-89
Social Capital

Social Leadership:
My First 100 days
by Julian Stodd

© Julian Stodd

Stand Up

DAY 81: CONSEQUENCE

Why don't we always intervene? Often because of learned consequence. When someone stands up and says '*this is wrong*', we have a choice. We can stay seated, staring at them, as they lose credibility and experience consequence, or we can stand up and stand alongside them. There may well be a consequence to this, but that consequence is shared.

I have a friend who was fired from her job for taking time out for fertility treatment: the decision was wrong, it was bad, colleagues told her it was bad, but nobody stood alongside her. Observing toxic culture is one thing, but it's valueless if we don't intervene.

How is consequence experienced? List three ways:

The first way we experience consequence is: _____

_____

Another way is: _____

_____

A final way is: _____

_____

The anticipation of consequence prevents us standing up: our Social Authority can give us the confidence (and backup) to stand.

Social Leadership: My First 100 days
by Julian Stodd

Your Survival Skills
© Julian Stodd

Social Age

DAY 82: SKILLS FOR THE SOCIAL AGE

List the three top skills that anyone in your business needs to survive and thrive in the Social Age. Perhaps they're specific technical skills, perhaps it's an ability to effectively network, maybe it's about promoting equality or simply having your LinkedIn page set up properly. What are your three top things?

The first is: _____

_____

The second is: _____

_____

The third is: _____

_____

Now talk to someone else: do they feel that they have mastered all of those things? What would their things be? How can you help each other?

Should your organisation have a list like this, or a curriculum to develop capability? If so, who will write it? Remember: Social Leaders have high Social Capital, they continually work to refine it and, crucially, they build it in others.

Social Leadership:
My First 100 days
by Julian Stodd

What is your etiquette?

© Julian Stodd

DAY 83: ETIQUETTE

One component of Social Capital is simple etiquette: do you have your rules in place, do the others around you?

For example, when people engage, when they share, when they connect, or help, how do you engage? What rules from the '*real world*' do we carry into social spaces, and which do we leave behind or reinvent?

It's important to actively consider these things: whilst digital spaces may '*feel*' less real, the emotional and trust impacts of our actions are very real. If someone on LinkedIn sends me a '*spam*' message, it feels inauthentic. By contrast, when someone on Twitter says something kind, it feels great: I actively take energy and strength from it.

So consider your etiquette: what are your rules?

One rule I have is: _____

_____

Another rule is: _____

_____

My third rule is: _____

_____

For example, if someone comments on something I have written, I always try to respond. If someone shares something, I try to say '*thank you*'. Am I perfect? No. But I have consciously tried to shape my rules. Actively consider aspects of your etiquette, and consider how you will help others to do the same.

80-89
Social Capital

Social Leadership:
My First 100 days
by Julian Stodd

Humility
is the foundation of
Social Leadership

© Julian Stodd

DAY 84: HUMILITY

Humility is the foundation of Social Leadership. But how do we learn to be humble?

It can certainly be expressed in a mindset (and, indeed, through our etiquette, the ways we thank or engage with people who challenge us). It's about recognising and acknowledging other people's views, even where we don't agree with them. It's about being willing to set aside our own views to give space to others.

Humility is experienced through actions: often a temptation for formal leaders is to carry their formal authority into social spaces, but that temptation erodes our Social Authority.

Who do you know who is humble? _____

_____

What makes you say that? _____

_____

What one thing that you do may stand in the way of your humility? It's a hard question I know, but try. Mine is that I sometimes like my voice to be heard in a debate. I am often unwilling to stay silent. But sometimes I should ask whether my voice adds signal, or just more noise. Or whether my voice is loud and silences others.

What is yours? _____

_____

80-89
Social Capital

Social Leadership:
My First 100 days
by Julian Stodd

CALENDAR

An

Action

© Julian Stodd

Day

DAY 85: AN ACTION DAY

Social Leaders have high Social Capital, but also develop it in others. Today is a day to help someone else succeed. Who can you help, and what can you do for them?

The person I can help is: _____

_____

The way I can help them is: _____

_____

_____

Consider this: are you helping them at a tactical, task-based level, helping them to clear a hurdle today, or are you helping them at a wider capability level, helping them to develop new skills, understanding or capability to perform better in the long run?

Have a balance: clearing tasks today is great, building capability for the long term is truly developing Social Capital.

How did you feel today? _____

_____

_____

80-89
Social Capital

DAY 86: EQUALITY

What does '*equality*' mean to you?

Equality means: _____

_____

_____

Equality is not something to strive for: it's something to fight for. All voices need to be respected and heard equally.

Ask two other people to join you for coffee: what does equality mean to them?

How are your views similar? _____

_____

_____

How are your views different? _____

_____

_____

Do you know where the gaps exist in your ecosystem? Does your organisation do what's mandated and legally called for, or does it do what is right? Every time?

Where do you stand? What will you fight for? _____

_____

_____

_____

_____

80-89
Social Capital

DAY 87: FEEDBACK

The skills that underlie high Social Capital are mastered through learning, rehearsal and inviting feedback. Talk to a colleague about Social Capital: use this as a chance to explain what it is, and perhaps to explain how you are undertaking your journey to become a stronger Social Leader.

Ask for feedback.

What do they see you doing? _____

_____

Did they have any advice? _____

_____

How did you feel about their advice? _____

_____

This may feel like a strange experience: what can you learn from it? Did you feel comfortable and able to explain what Social Leadership is? If not, how can you develop your story?

Social Leaders are embedded within their communities: it's where they co-create meaning and where they find their support and power. Without feedback, we are simply broadcasting. And broadcasting is an outdated model of communication.

Social Leadership:
My First 100 days
by Julian Stodd

Be
attuned
to your
Community

Listen
© Julian Stodd

Conversations
Conversations
Conversations
Conversations

DAY 88: LISTEN

As you refine your Social Leadership capability, you will be more attuned to your communities.

Listen.

What is the conversation taking place in the organisation today?

What do you hear people talking about? List three things, and say where you heard them:

1. _____

2. _____

3. _____

Now reflect. How did you get to hear these conversations? Were they in formal channels, or in your networks? How did you have the privilege of hearing these voices? Could you do anything to hear more of them?

Can you identify anyone who has not heard these stories, but who would benefit from hearing them?

If you answered 'yes', perhaps that person needs to develop their own Social Capital: perhaps your role today is to help them. Reach out and have the conversation: this will let you rehearse your 'pitch', and is an example of helping others to succeed.

80-89
Social Capital

Social Leadership:
My First 100 days
by Julian Stodd

Dont Just Observe Change

©Julian Stodd

DAY 89: TAKING STOCK

It's called 'Social Capital' because it's a currency, of sorts. Something that can be earned or spent. How are you doing in your accrual and waste? What's the balance?

We've spent ten days exploring this: do you feel you have changed, or have you simply observed the community around you?

Have I changed? YES ☐ NO ☐

Am I thinking about changing? YES ☐ NO ☐

Thinking is easy: if you haven't reached out, if you haven't tried these exercises, if you haven't refined and rehearsed your language around Social Leadership and Social Capital, you may simply be observing the challenge.

True change starts with mindset, but graduates rapidly to action. We are nearly 90 days into our journey: can you feel progress?

What is the key thing you have learned so far? _____

_____

What is your greatest frustration so far? _____

_____

What are you proudest of about this journey so far?

_____

Finally, reach out and thank someone who has supported you, by listening or helping you on this journey.

Lead with kindness and humility. And live those values every day.

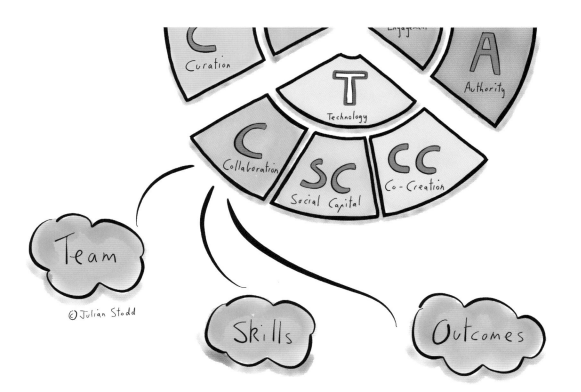

© Julian Stodd

DAYS 90 TO 99: COLLABORATION

Social Leaders start by taking a stance, they '*curate*' their space. They learn how to be powerful '*storytellers*', and how stories are '*shared*' widely, but wisely. By carefully growing and nurturing their '*community*', through their actions, they build '*reputation*', and hence are awarded '*Social Authority*'. With this authority, they '*co-create*' meaning within their communities, they develop high '*Social Capital*' in themselves and support it in others. They make their organisation more Socially Dynamic, equal and fair.

With this in place, they collaborate.

Collaboration means we understand the needs of the individual and organisation, and bridge the two. Collaboration requires us to recognise the validity in the views of others and be humble enough to modify our own.

If we are effective Social Leaders, we collaborate widely, to be successful ourselves, and to help others achieve success. For that reason alone, Social Leadership is not an aspirational or soft activity: it's purposeful and outcome focused. It just achieves those outcomes through Social Authority, not formal command and control.

Social Leadership:
My First 100 days
by Julian Stodd

Collaboration
© Julian Stodd

Inhibited   Or   Enabled

DAY 90: CONSIDERATIONS FOR COLLABORATION

We need our strong foundations in place for collaboration to occur, that's why it sits here, at the end of the circle (if circles have ends… the journey to Social Leadership is one of iteration and continual learning, so don't be surprised by the surprise to come…).

From your perspective, what is the most important consideration for collaboration to occur?

The single most important factor for collaboration to occur is:

_____

And what three things can inhibit collaboration?

The first thing is: _____

_____

The second thing is: _____

_____

Finally: _____

_____

Which of these things are in your power to address? We are moving to the point of irreversible action: are you confident you have your foundations in place? Social Leadership is lived, not worn as a badge or title.

Talk to your community: how does your answer match up against theirs?

Social Leadership:
My First 100 days
by Julian Stodd

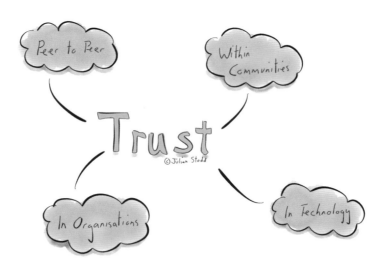

Peer to Peer

Within Communities

Trust
© Julian Stodd

In Organisations

In Technology

DAY 91: TRUST

To collaborate, we need trust. The initial research I'm doing around the Landscape of Trust indicates that trust resides in strong social ties, within our networks. How does trust relate to collaboration? Share a couple of lines on why you think trust is important.

Trust is important for collaboration because: _____

_____

_____

My answer would include this:

1. Consequence: when we carry out sense-making activity, when we collaborate, we share our ways of working and learning, we expose ourselves to risk. To collaborate is to expose ourselves to consequence, so I need to trust the people I collaborate with to respect the trust I show.

2. Collaboration is about more than time: it's about generosity of ideas, so trust is needed if we are to expose these inner thoughts.

People don't often talk about trust: consider making it an explicit part of your story as you set up and join collaborative communities. Be clear that you bring to the table not simply your presence and your time, but also your fragility and trust.

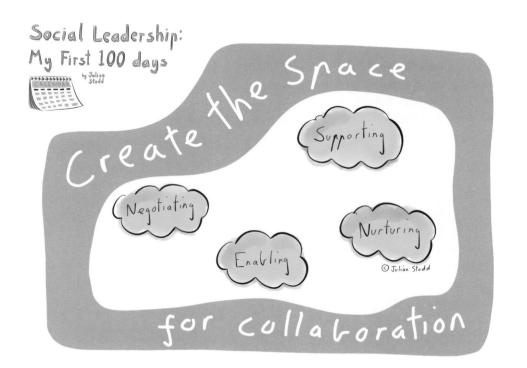

Social Leadership:
My First 100 days
by Julian Stodd

Create the Space

Supporting

Negotiating

Enabling

Nurturing

© Julian Stodd

for collaboration

DAY 92: NEGOTIATION

Collaboration involves negotiating the competing needs and desires of individuals and organisations: our role, as Social Leaders, may be not to have all the great ideas, but rather to nurture and develop the space and environment within which collaboration can occur.

This harks backs to humility being at the heart of Social Leadership: are you willing to find your power as the enabler of others, rather than simply being the loudest in the room?

How do we understand these conflicting needs? Through conversations: both formal and social. We find ways and spaces to bring people together.

Can you think of an intractable challenge, of two parts of your organisation that tend to fall to conflict? My example would be in the NHS, where we often see leadership and practitioners in conflict. If I was bold, I would say that this conflict means that neither side can hear or understand the reality of the other.

Where do you see conflict? _____

_____

What factors do you think feed this? _____

_____

_____

As a Social Leader, it will be your role to build a bridge here.

Social Leadership:
My First 100 days
by Julian Stodd

We need
both
Space
and
Permission

© Julian Stodd

Permission
Space

DAY 93: SPACES AND PERMISSION

You cannot force people into dialogue: but you can create the space for it to take place. Upon that foundation of dialogue, we can find space for collaboration.

To fully understand this, we must see the difference between 'spaces' and 'permission'. Space is the place for a conversation to take place, but 'permission' relates to the social factors that enable or inhibit it. When we have conflict or separation, space can be easy to come by, but permission is lacking.

For example, people who seek to cross the divide in opinion can be judged, not simply by the people that they talk to, but from within their community too, because the act of reaching out is viewed as a betrayal of trust, as crossing a line.

If we just wish to collaborate within a closed group, we don't need permission. To collaborate more widely, though, and to do so across boundaries, we need both.

How is permission found? _____

_____

In some ways, this is a question about where we find our strength.

Talk to someone else about this: how do you both understand conflict and collaboration?

Are your views the same or different? _____

_____

90-99
Collaboration

Complex Collaboration

DAY 94: FEELING IT

It may have become clear by now that I'm predominantly talking about complex collaboration, not about simply talking to someone you know, like and respect. To become Socially Dynamic, we need to open up new lines of understanding and collaboration around the organisation, crossing boundaries.

How will you know if you are collaborating effectively? List three ways.

I will know that I'm collaborating effectively if:

1. _____

2. _____

3. _____

Try to compare your answers to those of someone else in your space: were they similar, or different?

For me, I know if I am collaborating effectively if:

1. I am exposed to challenging views that differ from my own
2. I am willing to reconsider my position as I respect the views that I am hearing
3. I am not afraid to change my view, confident it won't be viewed as weakness, but rather as agility

How often do I feel this? Maybe not all that often, except in core communities that I trust.

Where do you feel that you collaborate most effectively?

_____

Where do you not collaborate effectively?

_____

The second answer may be a place to start, if you are feeling ready to move more deeply into practice: open up new spaces.

Social Leadership:
My First 100 days
by Julian Stodd

An Action Day

© Julian Stodd

DAY 95: AN ACTION DAY

Pick up a seemingly intractable challenge in your organisation and assemble a team of your strong social connections and people from other communities. '*Sense make*' ways you could fix it.

The challenge I am thinking of is: _____

_____

_____

_____

The outcome was: _____

_____

_____

_____

How do you feel about this? If you are talking to existing friends and colleagues, you are simply collaborating in known spaces.

If you feel a barrier to action, you may be observing your leadership journey, not actually embarking on it. Remember: Social Leadership is about action, about making your organisation better. You cannot do it without risk, and you cannot do it without action.

Think back to reputation. What reputation did you want? Are you on that journey? View today as one step. If your activity today feels slightly risky, and slightly unusual, you are probably winning.

Incidentally, if the organisation reacted to you trying to solve a problem by shutting you down, it may be resistant to change... but that's a whole other story.

Social Leadership:
My First 100 days
by Julian Stodd

CALENDAR

DAY 96: STORIES AND REPUTATION

To empower collaboration, we must recognise and respect those with whom we collaborate. We have thought about stories before. How will you recognise the input of others? In what spaces will you reward them?

As you collaborate, how will you recognise and show respect for the input of others?

_____

_____

Where will you share your stories of success? _____

_____

_____

Social Leaders #WorkOutLoud: this is the process by which they share the working, as well as the end result.

In the Social Age, we can build our reputation upon many different foundations: to be the person who creates conditions for collaboration, the person who awards respect and says '_thanks_', the person who enables – that's a great foundation.

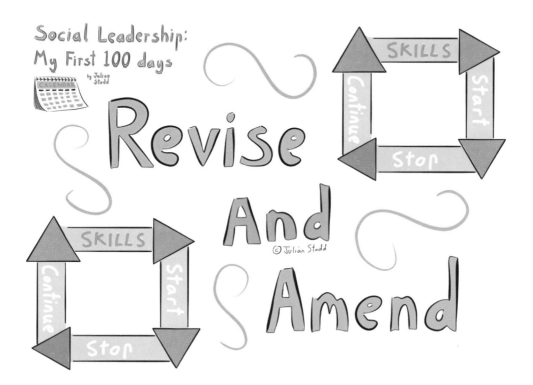

DAY 97: REVISING YOURSELF

As we collaborate more widely, we don't want to view what we do as '*success*', but rather as an opportunity for review.

The skills and behaviours we demonstrate today may not stay up to date if we don't revise and amend them. Part of our collaborative process should be to review our skills, review our communities, and review the outcomes we achieve.

What core skill do you think you need to strengthen?

What could you stop doing? _____

_____

_____

_____

Agility is about constant adaptation, as much about stopping doing things as it is about starting new things.

90-99
Collaboration

Social Leadership:
My First 100 days
by Julian Stodd

Remove the Friction

© Julian Stodd

DAY 98: IDENTIFYING CHALLENGES

Can you spot a place where people are not collaborating effectively?

What is the problem? _____

_____

What would solve it? _____

_____

How can you enable this change? _____

_____

Naturally, not all problems are easily solved: some require a budget, some require time, some require technology. But some reside in our minds alone.

With high Social Capital, with a reputation intact, with great storytelling skills, and with your Social Leadership mindset in place, these are the very challenges that you should be thinking about.

There is unlikely to be one single action you can take that will deliver wild success in your organisation.

Your challenge is to remove the friction from within the system. To take the individual grains of sand out of the gears. To be vigilant, not only within spaces you know, but to boldly venture into spaces that are unfamiliar.

Because to be a great Social Leader, you will be a bold explorer.

DAY 99: GENEROSITY

Social Leaders are generous, not only with their time, but through access to community, resource and ideas. They share without expectation of reciprocity. In collaboration, not only are they accepting of other people's ideas and differences, but they actively solicit them. They build diverse communities of ideas and welcome divergent thought.

Collaboration is an active skill: we could choose to passively wait for it to happen to us, or we can actively go out and make it happen. Collaboration is how you work, not a thing that is done to you.

What three things can you do to be more effective, active and generous in your collaborations?

One thing I can do is: _____

_____

The second thing is: _____

_____

The final one is: _____

_____

Which of these feels hardest? Who could help you with that? Start by asking them: collaboration to solve hard problems can build strong social bonds and earn trust.

90-99
Collaboration

Social Leadership:
My First 100 days
by Julian Stodd

Day 9
Day 11
Day 30
Day 19
Day 22
Day 51
Day 42
Day 63
Day 77
Day 87
Day 92
Day 100

Where Next?

© Julian Stodd

DAY 100: THE NEXT LEVEL

Here we are: Day 100. You have completed the first 100 days of your journey. You are on the way to becoming a Social Leader and if you have been sharing, if you have been engaging, then you have also helped others upon their journey too.

Social Leadership is not a formal qualification: you do not take the course and pass the exam. Nobody is going to give you a certificate with a clip-art picture of a gold cup on it. Nobody is going to thank you for this work in your annual performance review. And yet, if you live the values that we have discussed, your community will reward you, helping you to be more effective as you help them to succeed.

You will have the privilege of hearing the unheard voices, the hidden wisdom in your organisation. You will have access to ideas and resources. You will be part of a community.

But, best of all, if you are truly on the way to being a great Social Leader, you will have the respect of others around you: you will be championing the voices of those who have none. You will be driving an agenda of fairness and inclusivity. You will be known as someone who never avoids hard decisions. You will have earned trust.

What has been the easiest part of this journey? _____

_____

What has been the hardest part? _____

_____

Who will you talk to about Social Leadership? _____

_____

And, most importantly, what will you do next? _____

_____

DAY 101: THE EXTRA STEP

But… the journey does not stop here.

In *The Social Leadership Handbook*, the NET Model is represented as a circle, because the end of the journey is the start of the next chapter. We start with 'curation', but then we revisit it. We choose new spaces, we learn better storytelling approaches, we share with greater wisdom.

We inhabit new communities, we help them to thrive, we recruit others into them and help them succeed. We earn our reputation and tentatively explore our new Social Authority. As our Social Capital builds, we spend more time supporting others and thanking those who support us.

With co-creation comes energy, some of which we invest in our fight for greater equality and fairness in the world around us. We collaborate. And then we start again.

You are not the leader that you were: but you may not yet be the leader you can become.

Knowing what you know now, what will be your focus for your next 100 days?

_____

_____

_____

_____

_____

THE SOCIAL LEADERSHIP HANDBOOK

Maybe you came to this book via *The Social Leadership Handbook*, or maybe this 100-day Guide will spark your interest in Social Leadership further.

The Handbook itself is a definitive, illustrated guide in three sections:

'*Foundations of the Social Age*': explores the new reality we live in, a time of constant change, and the ways we can learn to thrive in it.

'*The NET Model*': runs through the nine components in great detail, expanding on 'what you need to do about it' for each one.

'*Stories of Application*': is a section on the wider context and how different organisations are attempting to embed the principles of Social Leadership.

You can order The Social Leadership Handbook from Amazon, or direct from the Sea Salt Learning website here: www.seasaltlearning.com

If you can't afford it, email me, and I'll find a way to get you one.

THANK YOU

Thank you to everybody who helped make this book possible by Crowdfunding it on Kickstarter. I wish you every success on your journey.

Christine Locher
Jussi Mozo
Arun Pradhan
Caroline Wood
Nicholas Ribeiro
David Slocum
Nicola Pierre
Céline Schillinger
Professor Simon Carley
Stephen Waddington
Shannon Tipton
Valary A Oleinik
Meri Robson
Hugh Reeve
Joe Mitchell
Sue Beckingham

Prosperity 24.7
Tim Pointer
Cheryl Johnson
Nancy Bacon
Scott Gould
Curtis Gilbert
Anthony Hornby
Christoph Schilling
Robin Lal
Kurt Ewald Lindley
David Archer
Kris De Ridder
Aude Latreille Phifer
Karen Moloney
Tom Wood
Sacha Luthi

David Jarrett
Lesley Scott Reid
Frank Meister
Dan Slee
Katie Marlow
Patrick Lamplé
Mark Arnold
Emilie Reitz
Jon Sellors
Joyce Nelson-Avila
@pubdonna
  - Donna Hewitson
Con Sotidis
Bill West
Cliff Madison Jr
Joshua Novelle

Nerida Talbot
Liz McQue
Stephen Bruington
Helen van Ameyde
Dave Lee
Amy Grieves
Mathias Vermeulen
Steve McQuaid
Chris Coladonato
Marc Spencer-Bowles
Natalie Passmore
Kristie Pretti-Frontczak
  - a fellow {r}evolutionary
Laura Pettitt
Sally Rhodes
Nick Armendariz

Rachel Challen

Fabian Szulanski

Sam Rogers

Julie Stitt

Henriette Kloots
  - Pink Coat

Ed Curley

Holly Till

Dan Hewitt

Eleni Latridis

Rebecca Foreman

Asi DeGani

Michelle Cole

Will Haywood

Kerstin Heydorn

Louis J. Prosperi

Bob Price

Simon Hallam

Tosca Bruno-van Vijfeijken

Guille R. Lorbada

Jo Dodds

Nick Wilding

Theresa Shaw

Nigel Paine

Katie Haniford

Neil Von Heupt

David Wallace

Julie Allan

Lisa Gee

Gina Rosenthal

Zsolt Olah

Tamási Andrea

Kenneth Mikkelsen

Sarah Able

Tatyana Skoraya

Martyn Stevenson-Read

John White

Susan Shaw

Victoria Clark

Petra Peeters

Krystyna Gadd

Lorna Clancy

Beni Boy

Lorraine Minister

Helen Louise Farmer

I would also like to thank:

Renee, for kindness

Hannah, for support

Sam, for the design